CARING FOR YOUR

JULIA BURTON-JONES ha
and Social Administration an
and Continuing Education. She spent several years
researching the issues of ageing and caring while working
for the Jubilee Centre in Cambridge. Between 1990 and
1992 she initiated and ran a series of training seminars for
churches, entitled 'Action for Family Carers', and she
has recently been involved in setting up the Carers
Christian Fellowship, a new group for carers. Her book
Caring for Carers was published by Scripture Union in
1992.

Overcoming Common Problems Series

For a full list of titles please contact
Sheldon Press, Marylebone Road, London NW1 4DU

The Assertiveness Workbook
A plan for busy women
JOANNA GUTMANN

Beating the Comfort Trap
DR WINDY DRYDEN AND JACK
GORDON

Birth Over Thirty Five
SHEILA KITZINGER

Body Language
How to read others' thoughts by their
gestures
ALLAN PEASE

Body Language in Relationships
DAVID COHEN

Calm Down
How to cope with frustration and anger
DR PAUL HAUCK

Cancer – A Family Affair
NEVILLE SHONE

Comfort for Depression
JANET HORWOOD

Coping Successfully with Hayfever
DR ROBERT YOUNGSON

Coping Successfully with Migraine
SUE DYSON

Coping Successfully with Pain
NEVILLE SHONE

Coping Successfully with PMS
KAREN EVENNETT

Coping Successfully with Panic Attacks
SHIRLEY TRICKETT

**Coping Successfully with Prostate
Problems**
ROSY REYNOLDS

**Coping Successfully with Your
Hyperactive Child**
DR PAUL CARSON

**Coping Successfully with Your Irritable
Bowel**
ROSEMARY NICOL

**Coping Successfully with Your Second
Child**
FIONA MARSHALL

Coping with Anxiety and Depression
SHIRLEY TRICKETT

Coping with Blushing
DR ROBERT EDELMANN

Coping with Bronchitis and Emphysema
DR TOM SMITH

Coping with Candida
SHIRLEY TRICKETT

Coping with Chronic Fatigue
TRUDIE CHALDER

Coping with Cot Death
SARAH MURPHY

Coping with Crushes
ANITA NAIK

Coping with Cystitis
CAROLINE CLAYTON

Coping with Depression and Elation
DR PATRICK McKEON

Coping with Postnatal Depression
FIONA MARSHALL

Coping with Psoriasis
PROFESSOR RONALD MARKS

Coping with Schizophrenia
DR STEVEN JONES AND DR FRANK
TALLIS

Coping with Strokes
DR TOM SMITH

Coping with Suicide
DR DONALD SCOTT

Coping with Thyroid Problems
DR JOAN GOMEZ

Coping with Thrush
CAROLINE CLAYTON

Curing Arthritis Exercise Book
MARGARET HILLS AND JANET
HORWOOD

Curing Arthritis Diet Book
MARGARET HILLS

Curing Arthritis – The Drug-Free Way
MARGARET HILLS

Overcoming Common Problems Series

Curing Arthritis
More ways to a drug-free life
MARGARET HILLS

Curing Illness – The Drug-Free Way
MARGARET HILLS

Depression
DR PAUL HAUCK

Divorce and Separation
Every woman's guide to a new life
ANGELA WILLANS

Don't Blame Me!
How to stop blaming yourself and other people
TONY GOUGH

Everything Parents Should Know About Drugs
SARAH LAWSON

Family First Aid and Emergency Handbook
DR ANDREW STANWAY

Getting Along with People
DIANNE DOUBTFIRE

Getting the Best for Your Bad Back
DR ANTHONY CAMPBELL

Good Stress Guide, The
MARY HARTLEY

Heart Attacks – Prevent and Survive
DR TOM SMITH

Helping Children Cope with Bullying
SARAH LAWSON

Helping Children Cope with Divorce
ROSEMARY WELLS

Helping Children Cope with Grief
ROSEMARY WELLS

Hold Your Head Up High
DR PAUL HAUCK

How to Be Your Own Best Friend
DR PAUL HAUCK

How to Cope when the Going Gets Tough
DR WINDY DRYDEN AND JACK GORDON

How to Cope with Bulimia
DR JOAN GOMEZ

How to Cope with Difficult People
ALAN HOUEL WITH CHRISTIAN GODEFROY

How to Cope with Splitting Up
VERA PEIFFER

How to Cope with Stress
DR PETER TYRER

How to Cope with your Child's Allergies
DR PAUL CARSON

How to Do What You Want to Do
DR PAUL HAUCK

How to Improve Your Confidence
DR KENNETH HAMBLY

How to Interview and Be Interviewed
MICHELE BROWN AND GYLES BRANDRETH

How to Keep Your Cholesterol in Check
DR ROBERT POVEY

How to Love and Be Loved
DR PAUL HAUCK

How to Pass Your Driving Test
DONALD RIDLAND

How to Stand up for Yourself
DR PAUL HAUCK

How to Start a Conversation and Make Friends
DON GABOR

How to Stop Smoking
GEORGE TARGET

How to Stop Worrying
DR FRANK TALLIS

How to Survive Your Teenagers
SHEILA DAINOW

How to Untangle Your Emotional Knots
DR WINDY DRYDEN AND JACK GORDON

How to Write a Successful CV
JOANNA GUTMANN

Hysterectomy
SUZIE HAYMAN

Is HRT Right for You?
DR ANNE MACGREGOR

The Incredible Sulk
DR WINDY DRYDEN

The Irritable Bowel Diet Book
ROSEMARY NICOL

The Irritable Bowel Stress Book
ROSEMARY NICOL

Overcoming Common Problems Series

Jealousy
DR PAUL HAUCK

Learning to Live with Multiple Sclerosis
DR ROBERT POVEY, ROBIN DOWIE
AND GILLIAN PRETT

Living Through Personal Crisis
ANN KAISER STEARNS

Living with Asthma
DR ROBERT YOUNGSON

Living with Diabetes
DR JOAN GOMEZ

Living with Grief
DR TONY LAKE

Living with High Blood Pressure
DR TOM SMITH

Making the Most of Loving
GILL COX AND SHEILA DAINOW

Making the Most of Yourself
GILL COX AND SHEILA DAINOW

Menopause
RAEWYN MACKENZIE

Migraine Diet Book, The
SUE DYSON

Motor Neurone Disease – A Family Affair
DR DAVID OLIVER

The Nervous Person's Companion
DR KENNETH HAMBLY

Overcoming Guilt
DR WINDY DRYDEN

Overcoming Stress
DR VERNON COLEMAN

The Parkinson's Disease Handbook
DR RICHARD GODWIN-AUSTEN

Sleep Like a Dream – The Drug-Free Way
ROSEMARY NICOL

Subfertility Handbook, The
VIRGINIA IRONSIDE AND SARAH BIGGS

Talking About Anorexia
How to cope with life without starving
MAROUSHKA MONRO

Talking About Miscarriage
SARAH MURPHY

Ten Steps to Positive Living
DR WINDY DRYDEN

Think Your Way to Happiness
DR WINDY DRYDEN AND JACK GORDON

Understanding Obsessions and Compulsions
A self-help manual
DR FRANK TALLIS

Understanding Your Personality
Myers-Briggs and more
PATRICIA HEDGES

A Weight Off Your Mind
How to stop worrying about your body size
SUE DYSON

When your Child Comes Out
ANNE LOVELL

You and Your Varicose Veins
DR PATRICIA GILBERT

Overcoming Common Problems

CARING FOR YOUR ELDERLY PARENT

Julia Burton-Jones

First published in Great Britain in 1995
by Sheldon Press, SPCK, Marylebone Road, London NW1 4DU

British Library Cataloguing-in-Publication Data
A catalogue record for this book is available from the British Library
ISBN 0-85969-742-8

Photoset by Deltatype Ltd, Ellesmere Port, Cheshire
Printed in Great Britain by
J W Arrowsmith Ltd.

For my parents, Yvonne and Keith

Contents

Acknowledgements x

Introduction 1

1 The context of caring 3

2 Making decisions 12

3 Finding help 25

4 Coping with relationships 42

5 Managing feelings 58

6 Discovering survival strategies 73

7 Reviewing the situation 83

8 Recovery after caring 97

Useful organizations 107

Further reading 111

Acknowledgements

In writing this book, I am indebted to countless carers who, over the years, have been willing to let me learn from their experiences. Most recently, members of the Carers Christian Fellowship, of which I am newsletter editor, have been a great inspiration. Three people who have added especially to my awareness of the needs of carers of elderly parents are my friends, Sheila Park, Hazel Clegg and Primrose McCann. In talking and corresponding with the carers who have kindly allowed me to tell their stories in this book, I have gained a richer understanding of the rewards and stresses of a life spent caring. I owe them heartfelt thanks.

My publisher, Joanna Moriarty, has given tremendous support and encouragement. I would not, however, have been able to complete this book had it not been for the kind and constant encouragement of my husband, Simon, and my parents, Keith and Yvonne Burton.

Introduction

This book has been written for anyone who carries responsibility for the care of a parent or parent-in-law. The nature of that parent's needs does not matter. They may simply be physically frail, they may have suffered a stroke or heart attack, or the gradual effects of arthritis, or perhaps they have some form of dementia. Neither is the level of your involvement of relevance. You may be giving round-the-clock nursing care, or you may be offering only occasional support. The important issue is that your parent's well-being is of concern to you.

This is not first and foremost a guide to help you care more effectively. It gives no advice on the practical details of nursing. Too many 'manuals' for carers focus their attention upon the person in need of care, while leaving the individual who supplies that care in the background. This book concentrates on you: your needs; your feelings; your aspirations; your dilemmas; your relationships. It hopes to offer suggestions for surviving, and even thriving, as a carer.

To illustrate different aspects of caring, I have included a number of stories of real carers who have kindly allowed me to recount some of their experiences. I have tried to conceal as closely as possible the identities of the carers concerned, using false names for each person mentioned. In every other detail, however, I have tried to give a faithful and complete account, and have checked my version of their caring history with each carer. I am grateful beyond words to these carers for their insightful and honest commentary upon issues of a deeply personal, sometimes painful nature. Their willingness to share their stories has been born out of a firm desire to help other carers.

The carers in this book are spread geographically throughout the UK – though I make no claim to offer a scientifically representative selection of experiences. The aim of including snapshots of the lives of real people has simply been to bring to life what caring can mean for individuals.

I hope this book will help in the decisions you are asked to make. My intention has been to highlight both the positives and the negatives of caring, so that you can better understand your own reactions. The contribution made by carers to our national life, and to the lives of very many individuals, is of incalculable value. Sadly, this contribution is often made at the expense of their own health and well-being. This guide aims to allow you to take your own needs seriously, so you can care more successfully – and, most importantly, so that you can enjoy greater personal fulfilment in your role and relationship with your parent.

1

The context of caring

Accepting a commitment to care at close quarters for an elderly or disabled parent may appear to be the outcome of a straightforward decision. Someone you love, to whom you may feel you owe a debt of gratitude, needs your help. There seems to be little alternative but to open your life, perhaps even your home, to a new area of responsibility. Rarely are such conclusions so simply drawn, however. As you consider the future, your thoughts are influenced by an array of factors, of which you may not even be aware.

As an individual, you bring to your decision to care personal circumstances which affect your ability to offer support to your parent. You bring your personality, your relationships, your work, your home and your aspirations. You bring also the history of your relationship to your mother, father or parents-in-law, with its rich catalogue of moments of intimacy and conflict. In this chapter, however, we consider the wider context which affects your deliberations in subtle and unseen ways.

It would be easy to feel that you are making an independent choice, free from external pressures. In fact, the society in which you live has formed within you a set of expectations, and has shaped you through the course of experience. It places tangible constraints upon your options. The choices before you are not the ones your counterpart would have faced 20 years ago. Nor are they likely to mirror the decisions a person in your position will make in 20 years' time. It may help to consider some of the ways in which changes in our society, and in family life, have a bearing on your own situation.

A changing society

The experience of longevity

You hardly need to conduct extensive social research to find out that the number of older people in Britain has increased dramatically over the course of the twentieth century. At the turn of the century, only six per cent of the population were of pensionable age, compared with 18 per cent in the 1990s (according to Government statistics). In 1906 a new-born boy could expect to live to 48 and a girl to 52, whereas boys born in

1990 had a life-expectancy of 72.3 and girls of 78.2.

From the point of view of caring, the significant effect has been that there are more and more older people reaching their 80s and 90s. Of those who do, a significant proportion live with a degree of disability. Many continue to live independently, but others need help with the tasks of daily living. These demographic changes are cause for celebration. Not only can we look forward to a longer retirement for ourselves, but we can also enjoy a deepening relationship with our parents into our later years. Our children can benefit from the love and care of their grandparents and great grandparents. Family life can span four or five generations.

People living longer, however, can also mean increasing commitments at a time of life when we assume our responsibilities will ease. It is frequently at the time when our children leave home and we're looking forward to greater freedom, that we find one or other of our parents or parents-in-law in need of extra support. Because so many older people now live well into their 80s, it is not uncommon to find yourself faced with multiple caring responsibilities which may last for many years. Some carers look after both parents at once, or for each in succession. They may also face commitments in other directions, towards their children and grandchildren, aunts, uncles, partners and neighbours.

One characteristic of disability in very old age is steady but slow decline. While medical science has been greatly effective in countering acute illness – for instance, through the use of antibiotics – conditions like Alzheimer's disease and arthritis have as yet no cure. Their effects can span decades, over the course of which the relentless decline in the sufferer is matched by the steadily waning energies of the carer. As the number of octogenarians increases, so the prevalence of forms of dementia continues to grow, affecting one in five of those over 80.

Increasing life-expectancy, then, means that you are far more likely to be faced with the need to find support for an elderly parent. It also may mean a commitment to caring which lasts several years.

Changing welfare policies

It is widely acknowledged that the bulk of support for older people comes from their families and friends, with welfare provision from the state representing a small proportion. Nevertheless, the role of formal institutions will shape significantly the experience you have of caring for your parent. In particular, the level of resources available to fund projects giving back-up to carers affects profoundly the day-to-day lives of families. The adequacy of services is a legitimate consideration in your decision over how best to care for your parent.

The choices at your disposal are influenced by overall policies for care in old age. Currently the strongest theme underlining these policies is the notion that it is preferable for frail older people to live in the community than to move into institutions. This belief, known as 'community care', has widespread political support and tends to reflect the preferences of older people themselves, who often fight strenuously against being taken from their homes and placed in long-term nursing and residential care.

The policy of community care was outlined in the 1990 National Health Service and Community Care Act. A key aim of this legislation was to put an end to the incentive for older people, who could no longer cope alone, to move to old people's homes. Social security benefits had automatically covered the fees for people in homes. The 1990 Act transferred the budget for these fees to the control of social services departments, who could then use them to pay for services in people's homes. While commendable in theory, the new system of community care is not always proving easy to fund. It can cost a great deal to provide help to people in their own homes, and often local authorities find their budgets do not stretch far enough. One response has been to levy charges for some services which previously cost nothing.

Unless resources to supply services in the community increase in line with the growing need for them, it could well be carers who find themselves at the sharp end of any deficit. Social services departments with limited resources tend to target those older people with no alternative sources of help. Where there is a carer on the scene, services may be assumed to be less urgently needed.

In 1995 a bill was introduced to Parliament designed to bring services and recognition to carers. This has gained support from all parties, though its effects remain to be seen. While it gives you, as a carer, the right to ask for your needs to be assessed by your local social services department, you may then only receive support if it is available in your area. The bill does, however, represent a further step in the slow march towards recognition of the role and needs of family carers.

In terms of your decision to care, then, it is as well to be aware of broader pressures on the welfare state which, despite rhetoric in support of carers, often make them a low priority when it comes to the distribution of services. Community care policies may cause you to feel pushed into providing the necessary support for your parent to continue living in the community, even against your inclination or ability. One contemporary trend, however, from which you can take heart, is the existence of an increasingly vociferous carers' movement. The Carers National Association is at the forefront of the campaign to broaden the support available to carers, and has achieved a good deal in raising awareness of carers' needs and speaking on their behalf. The social and political context is shifting constantly, but plays a vital role in your experience of caring.

Attitudes towards old age

Another area of social change which affects you, as someone caring for an ageing parent, is the way in which old age is viewed. Attitudes in society as a whole form part of the backdrop of your own situation, and may help to influence your decisions.

In many ways, then, to be growing old in the late twentieth century is an unenviable experience. Senior citizens feel quite naturally that they have earned a degree of respect, an expectation of care and comfort, in their later years – hopes which may not be fulfilled. During a life-time of work, they have often contributed to a system of social security which seems to have failed them at the very moment when they need its help. Levels of pension have fallen significantly in relative terms over the last two decades, so that many struggle to cover basic costs. Others feel incensed that the National Health Service, built with the support of their earnings, deserts them at the very time they need its protection; they witness their savings and capital dwindle in payment for nursing-home fees, which they had always assumed would be covered by the welfare state.

Besides this material disadvantage, however, lies an attitude of mind towards retired people which marginalizes and belittles their role. Despite the fact that many pensioners remain active in family and community life, contributing to the healthy functioning of society, their role is assumed to be of little worth. Because they tend no longer to contribute to the economy, due to the practice of fixed-age retirement, they are seen as a burden upon society, draining its resources. Popular culture belittles retired people, attaching unflattering stereotypes to them: the badtempered old woman; the foolish elderly gentleman; the sweet little granny. Because they have poorer health, declining eyesight and hearing, lower degrees of stamina, the conclusion is reached that their opinions can be of no value. They are seen as being in need of protection, like children, unaware of what is best for them. The wisdom accumulated over years of experience is overlooked.

Work with older people is accorded little status because of the 'ageist' practices and attitudes in our own society at this particular time.

Members of the caring professions on the whole prefer work with younger people. The wages of care assistants in nursing and residential homes can be shockingly low, and conditions of employment harsh. Visit a job centre in search of employment and you will find posts for care assistants available in abundance.

As a caring son or daughter, you doubtless balk at the low esteem in which older people are held. You know that the stereotypes tell only one side of the story. Your parent is doubtless far more than simply a drain on your personal resources. Your relationship with them is ideally one of mutual respect and love. Nevertheless, the fact that older people are devalued by our society cannot but affect your morale. When you invest time and energy in the pursuit of your parent's welfare, it hurts to find that role accorded little recognition. It may feel particularly demeaning to be caring for an older person if your previous roles in life have brought public prestige and a higher profile. Your present role may seem a disappointment. Such are very often the feelings of parents who take a break from burgeoning careers to care for young children, changing nappies and spoon-feeding their offspring! It is legitimate to acknowledge your struggle to come to terms with what can seem a humble and invisible role.

The positive response in your own life, however, is to challenge assumptions which dismiss the role of older people. Our society is indeed the poorer for its failure to bow to the wisdom of old age and to demonstrate, in policy and practice, the gratitude owing to its senior citizens for the contribution they have made.

Changes in family life

The effects of increased mobility

Family life has seen rapid and dramatic transformation this century. One trend which has greatly affected the ability of families to care for older members is the increase in mobility. Communities are becoming far less rooted. Many people now move away from their home towns for higher education, training or employment. It is far less common these days for adult children to live round the corner from their parents. Few of us look far enough into the future to ponder the implications of leaving home for the welfare of our parents, when they eventually hit disability and dependency. We scarcely even consider the impact on our own children of having grandparents living many miles away. In any case, more often than not, these are not issues of choice or preference. At a time of high unemployment, our priority must be to secure work which will give us an income.

When a parent falls ill or becomes increasingly frail, then, we are faced with a dilemma. Being a 'commuting carer' can produce intolerable demands. At the end of a working week, few of us would choose to undertake a long journey in order to look after a parent. On the other hand, the alternatives are no more attractive. Moving back to your home town may entail considerable risk – you may not easily find a new job. Moving your parent to the area where you live involves severing their links with a community which may be all they have known.

Mobility can wreck extended families and render caring for an older person all but impossible.

Changes in relationships

Another factor which has impacted upon the family's ability to care for frail older members has been the increase in relationship breakdown. Rightly or wrongly, women tend to take a larger share in caring within families, not just for dependent children, but also for disabled relatives. Often, then, older people have relied on daughters-in-law. When sons divorce, however, they may not remain close to their former wives. Divorced women often take on demanding roles, fitting their paid work to support their families around child-care arrangements. At breaking point already, they cannot cope with the extra pressure to care for a frail parent.

Divorce has another dimension. It may be the older person who is divorced. They then cannot rely upon their partner to care for them, so responsibility falls upon their children. Or it may be, as a further complication, that the parent in need of care is the one the children regard as the 'guilty' party in the marriage failure. It is not easy to be faced with giving care to a father whom you feel deserted or was unfaithful to your mother, or vice versa.

The situation we face in 1990s Britain, then, is vastly different from the reality of the early twentieth century, when marriages lasted a lifetime. Besides the instability of existing marriages, there is also the trend towards cohabiting as a prelude or alternative to marrying. It is difficult to predict the degree of responsibility which cohabiting couples may feel towards one another's parents. Certainly, caring for an older person can represent a very tying obligation.

Changing employment patterns

Perhaps the most significant change in employment patterns as they affect the care of older people has been the growing number of women in paid work, which has continued to rise steadily through the century. Significantly, it is expected that the next decade will see an increase in the numbers of women in their 40s and 50s who are in paid work (according to *Britain 2010*, a report published in 1991 by the Policy Studies Institute). This is the age-group most likely to face the possibility of declining health among their parents. It is not only the presence of women in the work-force that is significant, but also their motivation in their chosen careers. Research shows that women value greatly their role as paid workers. They often regard their work not merely as a source of income, but also as an area of fulfilment, challenge and social stimulation.

It is impossible and inadmissible to turn back the clock to the days when a woman's place was believed to be in the home. The women's movement has achieved a great deal in opening the world of work to women – though much remains to be achieved. Perhaps a greater challenge will be to open the world of home-based activity to men, to persuade society that caring (for young children as much as for older people) is a legitimate and rewarding role for men.

In the mean time, it tends sadly to be women who face the full weight of pressure to choose between their jobs and their loved ones. If you are a female reader, you should acknowledge this pressure to be unjust. There is no reason why you, as a woman, should feel a greater duty than a man to relinquish a hard-won career. If you take on caring to a point where it jeopardizes your work, let it be because you have chosen positively so to do, and not because you feel that society expects it simply because you are a woman.

The role of ideas

The discussion about changing levels of mobility, family breakdown and women's employment leads naturally to an analysis of the ideas which govern our choices. We may consider ourselves free thinkers, yet we are inevitably influenced by prevailing philosophies and fashions. Very often our apparent 'choices' are merely strategies which reinforce the economic climate in which we live – for example, we decide to take early retirement, but this is in the context of a surfeit in the work-force. Choices we believe to be morally defensible are sanctioned by undercurrents of thought. Swimming against the tide of these beliefs is seldom easy.

Notions of duty derived from our society shape our decisions. So to what extent does the duty to care for ailing parents remain sacrosanct, and how appropriate is it? A book written in 1989 by Jill Pitkeathley, director of the Carers National Association, bears the title *It's my duty, isn't it?*. Many carers are driven by this unquestioning sense of obligation. The adage enables some people to carry on in the face of considerable stress – but for others it is unwelcome. Reading this, you may react strongly against the notion that you have a duty to care for a parent whom you feel has failed you. You may argue that an accident of birth should not consign you to years of misery, enforced intimacy with someone who feels like a stranger to you.

The sense of duty upon which the edifice of welfare in our society rests, then, is by no means guaranteed into the next century. Many older people themselves resist the concept of burdening their children, and would rather opt for paid care from workers outside their immediate family. It is possible that the idea that families should care for frail older people could be replaced by the notion that greater distance between the carer and the person for whom they care is preferable.

For those from other countries of origin, the struggle to remain true to cultural norms can be particularly fierce. The alien values of the society around them can leave many minority ethnic carers feeling under pressure to deny their belief in the primacy of the wider family. The demands of employment fail to account for kinship obligations.

Conclusion

Faced with the possibility of caring for a parent, you do not stand as an individual in command of the situation before you. Myriad social forces contribute to your deliberations. Misplaced, abstract feelings of 'duty' rarely suffice as a motivation for caring. Indeed, it can be positively dangerous to accept a pressure to care in circumstances which are not propitious. A shortage of alternatives may cause you to feel guilty about declining such pressures, but you alone understand the dynamics of your own situation. You are the only person able to assess the history of your relationships with your parent or parent-in-law, and to weigh your other responsibilities against the need to care for them. As the next chapter will show, if you feel that your family life cannot sustain caring directly, this is no occasion for self-recrimination. External social pressures (such as employment and mobility) have significantly altered the capacity of each individual to care. Your decision is not only one of personal choice but also represents the outcome of social change. A caring relationship tends only to thrive when it results from the positive wishes of both the carer and the person who needs care.

2

Making decisions

In Chapter 1 we considered the context in which families in today's Britain make decisions on how best to care for elderly relatives. We shall now consider the factors to be taken into account before you make a decision.

The importance of planning

Many families are taken completely by surprise to find an elderly member, often the very linchpin of that family, in need of help. There seems to be a resistance towards any form of long-term planning for the care of older members of the family. Situations are allowed to drift, and only when they become desperate do we tend to apply our energies to seeking solutions. Why is the thought of looking ahead and forming contingency arrangements so alien to us?

The failure to plan partly reflects our desire to live in the present. The demands of daily existence are enough to absorb our time and emotional reserves. To be forced to look into an unknown, uncertain future can represent an unwelcome pressure, particularly if it carries with it the likelihood of additional responsibility. Another good reason for avoiding anticipation by several years, even decades, is the unease we feel over the possibility of our parents ceasing to be the active, independent individuals they are now. Our parents are those people to whom we may take our own worries and difficulties. The childhood belief in parental invulnerability dies hard in our adult years. We are troubled by the notion that one day, our parents may become dependent on us. The thought of this blow to their pride is disturbing. Neither can we gladly envisage them in a state of pain or weakness.

A further reason for burying our heads in the sand is that planning for these sorts of eventualities might interfere with the choices we wish to make today. Who wants to feel prepared for the possibility (which may never arise) of caring for an ageing parent if it means moving house, changing jobs . . . ? Given an opportunity to work abroad, for instance, how many of us would allow concerns for the future welfare of our as-yet fit parents to close off the chance of change and challenge?

The reality, however, is that thinking through these issues is often the means by which families can best prepare for caring. The outcome of policies of drift are frequently situations of chaos or injustice. When parents do eventually become frail and dependent, it is perhaps the child who lives nearest, or has fewest additional responsibilities, who ends up shouldering the caring exclusively. The traditional idea of an unmarried daughter inheriting the care of her parents in their final years, then, is not so far from the truth. For some inexplicable reason, there is often one member of a family who feels most keenly the pressure to provide support. This person may not necessarily be the best-equipped to give help, but, welcoming their willingness, other members of the family then feel discharged from any kind of duty or commitment.

Planning ahead can allow families to devise ways of sharing out responsibilities for caring more fairly, so that the onus does not fall unevenly. One member of the family may express a willingness to take on the primary role, while others can suggest strategies they hope to employ which would offer relief to that individual. Whilst it is probable that circumstances will change and plans will need adjustment, it helps greatly to know in advance of a crisis the preferences held by each family member. When it comes to the crunch, there should be permission for each person to change their mind and opt for a role other than the one they had intended, but it certainly is a well-proven fact that those carers who feel theirs was a positive decision to care are the ones who cope best with the demands involved.

The catalyst

The journey towards caring has two primary routes. One is a slow, winding road with the destination signalled well in advance. The other is a sudden plunge into unknown territory across rocky terrain. We shall consider each in turn.

Gradual decline

To put it plainly, caring may be the outcome of a parent's steady decline into dependency. From being a sprightly, capable pensioner, insulted by the mere offer of assistance, they slowly lose independence as a result of increasing infirmity. Medical advances can successfully stave off some limiting conditions, but we are mortal and our bodies begin to fail. For some, this obviously occurs sooner than for others, depending partly on factors such as previous work and environmental experiences.

There can be a progressive loss of sensory functioning. A large number of older people have a degree of hearing loss. There is also the possibility of declining eyesight which, in extreme cases, can lead to blindness. Other conditions can steadily undermine older people's mobility and dexterity: arthritis, multiple sclerosis and osteoporosis, for example, can make walking difficult; emphysema and angina create difficulty breathing and can gradually confine a person to their home. Then there may be mental health difficulties, like dementia, which may make it difficult for people to live alone safely. Conditions like Parkinson's disease have both physical and mental effects, and bring about progressive decline. Some simply grow increasingly frail, a noticeable reduction in energy and flexibility making day-to-day living a challenge. Often these complaints come in packages, and it is coping with multiple disability that can eventually rob the individual of their independence.

The situation where decline is slow but steady makes planning ahead easier. In the early days, minor adjustments to the older person's routine are all that is needed. As a caring son or daughter, you may feel the need to pay more visits, or telephone more regularly, to check that your parent is coping. As greater levels of dependency arise, tact and sensitivity are needed in offering and arranging more support. Conflict can arise if your parent is unwilling to acknowledge that they are struggling. Try to enter into how they must feel; identify with their frustration, anger and perhaps even humiliation. Accept that denial is a natural response on their part. Be prepared to catch yourself acting in ways which are over-protective. Well-meaning though you may be, it cannot be right to strip a parent of cherished independence merely to relieve your own anxiety. An older person's wish to remain independent is worthy of full respect. Persuasion, diplomacy and, above all, patience, are needed to convince your parent of the wisdom of accepting outside help. It is a blow to the pride to have strangers in the house doing jobs they have always done themselves.

At this stage, it is good to look into the future and imagine how you as a family might cope if your mother or father were to become unable any longer to live alone. Assess the potential of each member of the family to contribute to their care. Establish the older person's preferences – do they feel strongly against living with a son, daughter or grandchild, or react violently against the possibility of moving to a nursing or residential home? It may be useful to conduct some research into the level and nature of services available locally. Is there an effective system for giving support to families? Are there nursing homes which seem to have a particularly good reputation?

Along this winding route, constant adjustments will be needed. Arrangements which suffice at one stage may soon become inadequate.

There may be the need for your parent to move to more manageable housing – a flat or sheltered accommodation. If you are fortunate, you will have access to the expertise of a 'care manager' (see Chapter 3), probably a social worker, who can help the family reappraise your parent's situation at regular intervals, bringing in additional help that may become necessary.

Eventually, efforts to sustain your parent's independence may run their course. There may come a dawning realization that an alternative to their own home is needed. The difficulty is in identifying the moment at which this has become the case, particularly if your parent feels genuinely that they are managing. It is impossible to give a precise definition of a situation which has become untenable, as each person's circumstances vary – but there are some common indicators.

- A tendency for your parent to fall and be unable to get up. Besides the often considerable injuries sustained, there is then a suggestion of risk which needs to be taken seriously.
- The fact that your parent seems to be receiving every conceivable form of help, both from services and from family and friends, but is still unable to manage.
- The onset of dementia, which can cause an older person to place themselves in danger, for example, of causing a fire, or getting badly lost.
- There may simply be the sense that the older person is becoming increasingly housebound, has lost out in terms of social interaction, and feels lonely and depressed.

This is the moment at which factors discussed in the next section come into play in deciding how best to look after your parent.

Sudden need

The second route by which caring for a parent can occur is altogether more sudden, arising from a serious accident, or from an acute illness, or perhaps even from a bereavement. Perhaps a bad fall causes them to break a bone and be admitted to hospital, where doubt surrounds the possibility of their returning to their own home. Or they may suffer a stroke or heart attack and, from being fit and independent, become weak and frail with no guarantee of a full recovery. Alternatively, there may be the shock diagnosis of cancer necessitating urgent surgery and an intensive course of treatment. Or finally, your parent may be stricken with grief at having lost their partner or another close friend or relative, upon whom they have relied heavily.

It is in this kind of situation that decisions become fraught. There is little time to consider alternatives, with pressure to release a hospital bed which is in great demand. Sons and daughters can sense the expectation from medical staff that they will take their parent home with them, at least in the short term. This is no basis from which to make a rational decision. You will be feeling a storm of painful feelings. There is deep distress over the pain your parent is suffering, and a desire to protect them. You will doubtless feel a moral pressure to agree to care for them in your own home – to refuse would be to invite a flood of guilt and self-recrimination, if not outright hostility and accusation from your parent and any number of other interested parties.

But the implications of taking on the care of a severely disabled relative at a moment's notice are colossal. Under such conditions, how can you be expected to arrive at an arrangement which takes into account the needs of each person involved?

The consequences of a decision reached this way are felt afterwards. It can quickly become apparent that a hastily constructed response is unworkable. With all the will in the world, your desire to care for your parent in their hour of need may present impossible obstacles, necessitating a further period of deliberation. Far better to stand your ground, be honest with yourself and firm with those placing undue pressure on you, and reach a compromise which is hopefully acceptable to both yourself and your parent.

It is natural to wish to protect the person you love, and to shield them in your own arms, both literally and metaphorically, at a time when their world has fallen apart. But there are a variety of responses you can make as a loving daughter or son. To reach a realistic decision to search for a suitable nursing home does not represent failure; it is merely to accept a different kind of caring, one which does not place intolerable demands upon you, thereby damaging your relationship with a person you love. Caring is composed of more that just 'caring for' a person. The most important component is 'caring about' them. This you can continue to do wherever your parent lives.

Peter's professional interest in the care of people with dementia preceded his personal involvement. As a Methodist minister, one aspect of his work was to give pastoral care to elderly people in a local psychiatric hospital. When Alice, Peter's mum, was diagnosed as having Alzheimer's disease, he knew what to expect.

Alice was widowed when Peter was only seven and when his older, adopted sister Jenny was 15. In November 1992, a bogus water-board representative conned his way into Alice's home and burgled her. This was thought to have acted as a catalyst in the onset of dementia. The first sign that all was not well came with undue forgetfulness. Then Alice began to hoard things, such as dirty washing. Her eating habits began to give cause for concern. Next she started to wander, especially at night. She would make her way to church and wonder why there was no service. She would forget which day it was, or have a doze and believe she had woken the following day.

Eventually, Peter and Jenny's concern over Alice's personal hygiene and safety prompted her GP to call for an assessment. Home carers were assigned to Alice, but she refused to allow them to enter her home. Christmas 1993 was a painful time for Peter. During her stay with Peter's family, Alice was disorientated and aggressive towards Peter. He was advised to refrain from having Alice to stay. In the New Year, Alice began day-care, but was often unwilling to go and became aggressive with the driver who took her. The situation came to a head one night in March 1994, when Alice was picked up by the police at 3 a.m.. Three weeks in the local hospital were followed by a move to a nursing home.

Peter and Jenny found themselves torn over whether or not to move Alice to one of their homes. Because both had very young children and demanding jobs, they felt it was impossible. They feared that Alice's aggressive spells would have a bad effect on their children.

Although he is grateful that Alice still knows him and senses he is special to her, Peter finds visits extremely painful, and feels intense pangs of grief. Alice's illness has brought to the fore feelings suppressed over the years, such as the pain over his dad's death. Counselling has helped Peter come to terms with some of these issues. He finds he is in a better position now to support other families, but that coming into contact with their pain brings his own feelings to the fore. He dreads Alice forgetting who he is; he feels that losing his mother before death is what hurts most.

Factors to consider

1 Your relationship with your parent

Firstly, and most importantly, you must consider your relationship with your parent. However promising other circumstances may appear to be, unless a bond of understanding and respect exists between you, enforced intimacy is likely to harm your relationship and each of you as individuals. Caring can place extreme demands on a person. Without adequate reserves of love and commitment it becomes difficult to sustain the pressure. This is not to say, of course, that all carers are saints. We all have moments of frustration and despair, but caring relationships which are healthy are sturdy enough to survive when buffeted by the storms of life. Don't even consider having your parent to live with you if your only motive is to prevent your inheritance disappearing as payment for residential or nursing-home fees.

You alone can measure the quality of your relationship with your parent. No outsider has sufficient information to allow them to enforce a decision upon you. There may be good reasons why the prospect of caring intimately for your mother or father fills you with alarm or disgust. You may have experienced abuse at their hands. Perhaps you feel they neglected you as a child. You may have spent your entire adult life striving to break free of their disapproval, or the effects of their cruelty. If your feelings towards your parent are ambivalent, or even outwardly hostile, you need to think very carefully about accepting responsibility for their care.

There is the possibility, of course, that offering care to a parent with whom you have always been in conflict will provide you with a chance of reconciliation. You may wish to restore your relationship with them before it is too late. Or perhaps you welcome the opportunity to renew a deeper friendship with a parent to whom you have become a stranger in adult life. To an extent, you take a risk. You may well regret your choice and have to live with unfulfilled aspirations. You may well never hear your mother or father telling you how proud of you they are. Even in the face of disappointment, however, you might still be relieved that you at least tried to make things better.

Feelings towards in-laws are different altogether, and vary considerably. You may feel that your parent-in-law has never truly accepted you as an appropriate partner for their child. This may have caused you to feel underlying resentment over the years since you met your partner. You may find their way of thinking very different from the ideas with which you grew up. The debt you feel you owe them is much smaller than it would be for your own parents, who have loved and nurtured you since childhood. You may even feel you have scarcely known them, having seen them relatively infrequently before their illness – and you may then have reservations about giving intimate care to a person who seems little more than a stranger.

On a brighter note, it is the love and gratitude of many sons and daughters that enables them to bear gladly the demands of caring. Many carers will say that they feel it is their duty to care for their parent, and that they value the opportunity to repay a little of the kindness their parents have shown them. For these people, it seems the most natural thing in the world to welcome their mother or father into their home, or to give extensive support while their parent remains in their own home. And the rewards, in terms of relationships, of a decision to care can be very great. Every carer has their moments of depression and exhaustion, but many cherish the depth and warmth that sustains their friendship with the person for whom they care. Many value the contribution their parents make to the happiness and development of their own children, and turn to their mother or father, mother-in-law or father-in-law, for advice or comfort in the trials of day-to-day life. They do not see this relationship as uneven or one-sided. These carers miss their parent profoundly when they die; such sons and daughters speak about how much caring has changed them and enriched their lives.

If you decide to accept extra responsibilities for the care of your parent, you may well know a deep sense of satisfaction in developing a relationship which matters greatly to you. First, though, you need to look honestly at your relationship with your parent or parent-in-law, assessing its strength and quality, measuring its capacity to withstand intimacy and stress.

2 Your health and personality

Consider next your own health. Are you physically and mentally up to the job of looking after someone who may have high dependency needs, if not now then at some stage in the future? Nursing a sick person is strenuous work. You may have to lift them, to change their bed frequently and launder extensively. There may be a wheelchair to push. Your parent may require help with feeding. If a dementia sufferer, they may be constantly on the move, in a ceaseless energy of activity. How could you cope with broken nights?

Here again you must be truthful and face up to your limitations. There is no shame in having your own health problems which may ultimately make it impossible for you to nurse a sick person. If you have back trouble, for example, it would be ill-advised, even dangerous, to contemplate lifting a heavy person on a regular basis. Also, if you have psychological difficulties, it may be very difficult for you to offer a high level of care. Caring can involve stress, which can aggravate conditions like depression and schizophrenia.

Related to these factors are issues of personality. You may simply feel that, as a person, you are poorly equipped to be engaged directly in nursing a sick person. If you are a quiet person who has lived alone for many years and cherishes the privacy and peace this gives, you may find it impossible to take on the constant and inescapable demands of a sick person. Or perhaps you're not patient enough and would all too easily lose your temper, with the risk that you may harm your parent. Be true to yourself. Acknowledge your potential, physically and mentally, to care for your parent or parent-in-law. It is far kinder in the long term to accept early on that you are capable of giving only limited support, than to take on arduous full-time commitments, only to find very quickly that the situation is unworkable.

3 Other practicalities

There are other practicalities to be borne in mind. Chief among these is the question of geography. A separation of many miles between your home and your parent's will affect to no small degree the potential for you to provide care. Caring at a distance can be an option. It is not uncommon for people in full-time work, among other commitments, to spend weekends travelling 'home' and seeing to a parent's shopping, housework, washing and gardening. But this arrangement is exhausting, and difficult to sustain over a long period.

Other options, though, may appear drastic. Perhaps you feel the solution would be to move to your parent's area of the country, so as to care at closer quarters. The upheaval this represents is colossal. It may involve putting your house on the market with no guarantee of a sale. It might involve uprooting other people – your children or partner. It might entail leaving a secure job with no promise of a new one. If you decide to move on a temporary basis, you face uncertainty. You cannot know how long your parent will need your support.

It can seem easier, then, to apply gentle pressure in persuading your mother or father to move nearer your home. Although it may seem that they have fewer ties, you do need to consider the effect on them of leaving an area they consider to be their home. How would the loss of a familiar environment, with its store of memories and circle of friends, affect their health and well-being? How fair is it to insist they uproot and live with you to satisfy your own complex feelings of guilt and anxiety?

Then there are other practicalities besides geography. Do you expect your parent to continue living in their own home, with an increase in the help you offer? How easily could this be achieved? Would you have the time effectively to run two households? Do you have adequate transport between your house and theirs? If your parent is to move to your home, how suitable is it for a disabled person? How many steps are there? How narrow are the doors? Would it be possible to adapt it? You may need advice from an occupational therapist. Also, is the house large enough to accommodate an additional person?

Again, on a practical note, there are financial calculations to be made. Could you afford to have your parent or parent-in-law living with you, especially if it meant reducing the hours you work, or leaving your job altogether? Is your life-style compatible with theirs? Could they adjust to the hours and company you keep? Or could you rearrange your life-style at all?

4 Counting the cost

You must work out whether the sacrifices you will need to make to care for your parent or parent-in-law seem to represent a price worth paying. For you will have to make sacrifices, in all likelihood. And if you take on added responsibilities, it is not only your own life that will change, but also the lives of other people you are close to. What would be the consequences, for instance, of giving up your job, if this becomes necessary? Could you live with the prospect of losing income, promotion opportunities, pension entitlements, status, friendship, stimulation . . . ? Is this a cost worth incurring in order to be available to care directly for a loved one?

What other areas of your life would be affected? Is it possible to predict the impact of caring on your other relationships – with your children, your partner, your friends? If it is your parent-in-law who needs help, you need to consider how your relationship with your partner might be affected by an increasing involvement with their parent: will caring put unwelcome strains on your marriage as you become resentful towards your partner for your added burden of care? Consider too how caring might affect your social life. Caring will restrict you. It is a good idea to think through in advance which areas of your life may lose out, so that you are not taken by surprise or filled with resentment later on.

The honest approach is to admit, if you feel it, that caring for your parent in your own home will adversely affect your children, for example. Perhaps you feel the need to protect your children from some of the less pleasant symptoms of your parent's condition. Own this as your reason for deciding against moving your parent to live with you, and don't let others cause you to act against your better judgement. You are the best person to assess your family's capacity to absorb caring. It may seem hard to have to choose one relationship above another, but sadly this is sometimes unavoidable.

5 *The other options*

Another element of your decision will be a consideration of the various available alternatives. Having your parent to live with you is unlikely to be the only available option. Neither are you the only potential source of support. The next chapter will look at the process by which an assessment of your parent's needs – and indeed of your own needs – can be made. This professional help is vital in reaching a decision which has the best possible outcome for each person involved. Without it, you are in a poor position to weigh up possibilities.

There is a temptation, when surveying the choices that present themselves, to take control of the situation and overrule your parent's desires. Your perspective differs from theirs. Your priority may well be to ensure their safety at all times, which may lead you to conclude that the best form of care for them would be a residential option. This, however, may be the very outcome which your parent is desperate to avoid. Perhaps there are ways of increasing the level of support they receive at home. Or you could explore the possibility of some form of sheltered housing, offering peace of mind to you and safety to them – but not at the cost of their independence.

Other possible arrangements might involve an alternative to your accepting complete responsibility. Other family members could be asked to play their part, so that the commitments are evenly distributed. The prospect of receiving regular help from relatives, or even from neighbours or friends, may be a critical factor in allowing you to accept a primary role in caring.

Julie was 28 when her marriage failed, and it seemed the most natural step for her to return to her parents' home. Julie speaks of her parents with a passion of affection which makes you want to meet them. She describes their family life as very close and harmonious. She was always grateful in adult life that they refrained from interfering in her affairs, and instead gave unfailing support and encouragement.

Stanley, Julie's dad, was not well. He had emphysema and developed cancer. He eventually had a colostomy. For five years, Julie cared for him, but their relationship was always a mutual one. Stanley was a tower of strength throughout Julie's divorce proceedings. Towards the end of his life, she remembers happily his insistence on shopping with her for her birthday present. It was a desperate struggle – Stanley was not well enough to go out – but the watch they chose together that day remains Julie's most treasured possession.

While Stanley's health deteriorated, Julie's mum, Iris, became ill. She experienced hardening of the arteries and arthritis, and was later to suffer dementia and become incontinent. Julie felt genuinely grateful for the opportunity to repay something of the love and commitment she had received from both parents. She takes pride in the fact that she managed to care for her mum at home for over nine years, despite regular advice from her GP that the strain was too great. Indeed, she struggled throughout to let go when it became necessary for Iris to attend a day-centre, and then, towards the end, move to a nursing home. It felt to Julie as though she was giving her mum away.

It is just a year since Iris died, so the sense of loss is still raw for Julie. Immediately after her mum's death, Julie felt unable to face life without her. She recognizes that, throughout the time she was caring, she faced continual grief. It was so painful to see the people she loved suffering. And it was difficult to come to terms with the fact that she and her mum seemed to be swapping roles, with Julie becoming the carer for the person who had always been her support. She is thankful, though, that her mum was able to recognize her right up to the end of her life. She had dreaded a time when her mum's dementia robbed her of the awareness that Julie was her child.

Julie expects to feel fragile for some time. She reacts badly even to minor stresses, and finds it difficult to summon up the energy to spend time away from home. She would like to meet up with an old school-friend in her home town, but can scarcely face the thought of packing and travelling. She realizes her life must now fall into a new pattern, one which allows her greater freedom – but it seems strange no longer having her caring as a focus. Mental energy and coherence seem hard to find.

Julie hopes that the future might hold romance. Perhaps she will be able to renew a love affair with a man from South America whom she met shortly after her marriage broke up. Certainly, he still longs for them to be together. In the mean time, the death of her parents has left a colossal gap in Julie's life which she is slowly trying to fill.

Conclusion

Reaching a rational decision on such an emotive issue, you may feel, is scarcely possible. It is easily governed by the immediacy of your feelings. You may be overcome by a powerful sense of duty and obligation. Or the overwhelming grief and concern for your parent may be compelling you to put your own life on hold in response to their needs. However calculated and cold-hearted it may appear, however, planning and careful preparation at this stage may save heart-ache later on. You are less likely to feel trapped in an inescapable caring role if you can identify a moment at the start when you were able to make a positive decision to offer support to your parent.

In this difficult time of decision-making, it helps to be able to talk about your feelings and plans with someone who understands, and can help you see the situation clearly. In an ideal world, you will want to discuss with your parent what is best for them and for each person affected. If you are unable to talk with your parent, because of aspects of their disability or of your relationship with them, try and find another confidante. Many carers find their partners invaluable aides in their deliberations. Others turn to their GPs for advice, or seek out the counsel of a social worker. A brother or sister, or good friend, or perhaps someone you know who has been a carer, may provide a listening ear and timely suggestions in your quest for a solution.

In the end, however, the decision is yours. You are to live with the consequences. Your resources offer the key to the effectiveness of a caring situation. If you decide to care at a distance, don't allow others to fill you with guilt. If you decide to offer intensive care to your parent, know that you are not alone, that nearly 7,000,000 people in the UK care for elderly and disabled relatives. The role you have chosen is making a vital contribution to our society. You have selected a road with many hazards, but one which also promises a vista as yet unseen and filled with unexpected delights. Your first task is to see that you receive every available source of help to enable you to play your role and to survive. The next chapter offers some ideas for gaining help.

3
Finding help

Barriers to receiving help

Our society recognizes, in theory if not always in practice, that carers are an important group of people making a vital contribution. It acknowledges too that it is unfair to expect them to labour unhelped in the care of their loved ones. A system of support, therefore, does exist, albeit underresourced in some areas and unevenly distributed. Despite the availability of services designed to help them, however, many carers cope alone with the demands of their role.

1 Recognizing the role

A major hindrance is the lack of awareness among many carers that they have a recognized role. The word 'carer' itself has an unfamiliar ring, and is not something with which you may naturally identify yourself. You may feel more comfortable describing yourself simply as the child of your parent, rather than their carer. Accepting the label 'carer', though, may be the key to gaining help: 'I am a carer and therefore have a claim upon services provided by the Government for carers'. It will also help you to identify with other people in your position, even if they are caring for a child or partner, rather than a parent. And perhaps calling yourself a carer will help you feel you have a status in society, akin to the identity which a job gives people.

2 The reluctance to ask

Another tendency inhibiting carers in their quest for help is a feeling of guilt and failure. To ask for support may seem like an admission of defeat. It may seem tantamount to confessing you cannot cope, with the possibility then that your parent will be taken into the care of another agency, highly unlikely though this may be. Alternatively, it may appear that you are letting your parent down, not living up to their expectations, or exposing them to the indignity of outside assistance.

Is asking for help, though, truly a dereliction of what you deem to be your 'duty'? Perhaps you are suffering from an overdeveloped sense of responsibility which is being fed by unrealistic expectations of your own capacity for hard work. It is helpful to think in terms of the contribution of professional carers. People who are paid to work as nurses, doctors, home-helps and social workers are never asked to do without breaks for rest and recreation. Though many claim to work over-long hours, they nevertheless work shifts which alternate with periods away from the heavy demands they face. Would you invest your confidence in a doctor who had worked day and night for weeks on end without a break?

If you fail to heed the wisdom of showing yourself kindness and consideration, you store up for yourself trouble in the years to come. Tragically, the consequences of excessive stress often only strike carers once their relative is no longer in their care. For years they may have pushed themselves beyond the limits of human endurance, accepting constant pressure and enjoying little sleep or relaxation. The spectre of complete physical and mental breakdown threatens the equilibrium of a caring situation for those who ignore the warnings of their bodies. How sad for carers who have poured every last ounce of energy and person-hood into the task of sustaining a loved one, only to find their labours wasted, their own strength spent and their parent taken away and placed in the care of someone else.

Rid yourself of the idea that you are letting the side down in requesting what, after all, are likely only to be modest amounts of formal or informal help. This is not an issue of pride, it is a sensible precaution which will enable you to function as a carer for longer – and maintain your sanity into the bargain. No one gets away with pretensions to be superhuman for very long!

3 Inertia and exhaustion

A slightly different, but equally common reason for carers to go without the help that is rightfully theirs, is sheer inertia. Call it exhaustion or apathy, there is a real sense in which the struggle to manage each day's set of tasks and challenges occupies every waking minute. Carers suspect that tracking down appropriate services may entail more bother than they are worth. The thought of picking up the phone and entering upon a frantic chase to find the relevant office fills many with horror. The prospect of hours of sweat and toil over incoherent application forms is abhorrent. At the end of the day, carers fear that their efforts to identify help will cost them dearly in terms of both time and energy, with no guarantee, in the long run, that support will be forthcoming.

Fortunately, the Government is aware of the minefield which carers face in seeking help. Changes are afoot in the system of arranging packages of support for carers. More will be said of this later in this chapter. Take heart. The process may yet become simpler and more user-friendly. Realistically, services are rarely going to be tailored to suit your situation exactly. But I wager that you will not regret the endeavour involved. Even minimal levels of back-up can make an incredible difference to a caring situation.

4 Being 'indispensable'?

Yet another excuse for ignoring the possibility of enlisting help is the belief that you alone understand your parent's needs. Others will, in all likelihood, care less sensitively than you. They will not instinctively know how to respond to your parent's requests. You are indeed the expert when it comes to the care of your parent – but this does not mean that you are indispensable. Your parent will adapt to variations in care, and is unlikely to be the worse for seeing a new face from time to time. They might even benefit from the stimulation of meeting somebody new.

Perhaps clinging to the idea that your parent cannot manage without you has more to do with your own sense of identity than their needs. It can be difficult to learn that someone from whose care we draw meaning in life, is quite safe in the hands of another.

5 Parental reactions

The final factor to explore in the list of things which may inhibit your search for support is probably the most powerful. Countless carers go without essential help because of resistance they meet in their parent. You may still stand in awe of your mother or father, and continue to fear their disapproval. If so, you may lack the courage to go against their wishes in asking for help. On the other hand, you may identify only too well with their reservations over enlisting outside help. You can acknowledge their fear over the possibility of accepting intimate care from a stranger. You agree with them that this could involve injured pride, loss of dignity, loss of comfort. You do not wish to inflict this unwelcome trial on a person you know to be suffering considerably already.

However reasonable and understandable your parent's objections may be, however, this is the moment to stand firm. For the sake of your own preservation, you may need to cultivate a little distance and detachment which allows you to avoid being ruled by their feelings. However much you wish to keep caring in the family, so to speak, it would be foolhardy to punish yourself unnecessarily by agreeing to unreasonable demands. If you refuse to keep a little time each week which is yours and yours alone, you risk losing a sense of who you are. In the long term, this may cost you dearly; you need to have a life left after your parent has gone. In any case, you will care all the better if you have time for your own interests and friendships. It can seem that your parent is the person in the frame who counts most. Attention can appear to be focused exclusively on them. But you matter too. You also have needs, albeit less obvious or immediate needs. Don't let failing self-esteem persuade you that this is not the case.

Where to go for help

Help from friends and family

Many carers prefer to turn to members of their family for the support they need in caring for their parent. If your mother or father still lives in their own home, you may devise a rota for visiting them, whereby you undertake to be 'on duty' several days of the week, while a brother or sister covers the other days. It may be that your parent still has their partner to care for them, and that your role is one of relieving the parent who cares.

If your parent lives with you, perhaps you can reach an arrangement with another relative which allows you to have regular breaks. A brother or sister could be asked to spend a day, or even half a day, each week looking after your mother or father. Or perhaps you would rather they took over for an entire weekend or week every so often, thus giving you a longer rest and allowing you to go on holiday. This solution tends to be the most sensible approach where the brother or sister lives some distance away.

At this point it would be dishonest and unfair not to mention the disappointment many carers face in enlisting help from members of their close family. You may assume, at the point of deciding to care for your parent, that relatives will rally round and do their share of helping out. It can be a crushing blow to discover, then, that those close to you see your decision as their opportunity to opt completely out of contributing. It may be that they lack imagination and are unaware of the strains you face – or they may even be guilty of a callous disregard. Whatever the reason, it is by no means uncommon for carers to be left struggling single-handed with a person for whom they consider others to share obligations.

Other factors can impede arrangements for sharing care. Your brother or sister may live in unsuitable accommodation. They may have other responsibilities which preclude them from helping. They may be in poor health themselves. Or they may live at a distance from your parent's home which makes their potential as caring colleagues negligible.

The disillusionment you feel as a result of neglect by close family can be hard to handle. This may be intensified by the real possibility that your parent sees the situation differently. It can be frustrating when a parent idolizes one of your absent brothers or sisters, living for their rare visits, and presenting to them a charming and affectionate side which you never experience. It is almost inevitable that you slip into intense resentment towards a sibling who offers nothing, while you labour tirelessly without thanks or recognition.

Family agreements over sharing care can work extremely effectively – though it is wise to expect problems. For those whose families are little help, or who lack close relatives, applying to other sources of support is the next option.

Diane had seen her mum, Doris, go through numerous spells of ill-health. From when Diane was only eight, Doris had had several operations to remove lumps from her breasts. Finally, when Diane was 14, Doris had a complete mastectomy. Several years later she had a hysterectomy too. Despite her poor health, Doris continued to care with great commitment for her own mother who lived next door.

It was seeing her mum's example which prompted Diane to care for her as she grew more frail in later life. Having married at 22, had three children in quick succession, and then seen them reach adolescence, Diane was ready for something different. But she found herself with a mother whose physical and mental health was deteriorating. At 75, Doris went into hospital for a bowel and bladder repair. Then, two years later, she had a heart attack. She began to find the stairs up to her first floor sheltered flat difficult to manage. So, in May 1991, Doris moved to a ground-floor flat. Within a year she had become psychotic and paranoid.

Diane and her sister took it in turns to have Doris to stay with them until she was well enough to return home. They witnessed Doris's weight fall dramatically, so that she weighed only five stone by the time she died in September 1993. Besides sharing care for Doris between them, Diane and her sister had the help of a home-care aid at lunch times and a home-help on Mondays.

Diane felt she was unworthy of her mother's gratitude and esteem. She felt she was too selfish to deserve thanks. It comforted her, however, to sense that she added to her mum's quality of life in a special way, in that she would spend time just sitting with her mother and listening. Together they went back to childhood and traced Doris's life. Diane took photographs of places Doris had lived and they put together a book telling her story. The love and understanding between them grew.

Doris often reassured Diane that she would not regret the time spent caring. Diane realized that her mum must also have struggled when she cared for her own mother. Looking back, Diane agrees that time spent caring for an elderly parent is never wasted. A year ago, following her mum's death, she suffered a heart attack, but she has plans for the future. She has returned to an ambition which she postponed when she married and had her first child. She is studying for a degree, and is hoping to use music in a therapeutic setting.

Diane's only regret over Doris's final years concerns the damage she suspects was caused by her mum's psychiatric treatment. A fortnight before she died, Doris had a further heart attack and was taken off all medication. Her psychotic symptoms then immediately vanished. Diane and her sister had wondered all along how effective the drugs had been.

Help from outside the family

Persuaded now of the need to seek help, the task before you is to find out about services available to carers, and to take steps towards receiving them. The good news is that finding help is becoming an easier process for carers, thanks to recent legislation altering the organization of care in the community. The bad news, as you might expect, is that services for elderly and disabled people living in the community are in great demand, and local authorities often lack the resources to respond adequately.

As a result of the National Health Service and Community Care Act of 1990, a new system for organizing services for disabled people has been in operation since April 1993. In cases where a disabled person living in the community is in need of support, their needs are assessed by their local social services department (social work department in Scotland, social services board or trust in Northern Ireland). As a carer you can ask for an assessment of your parent's needs. Also, under the 1996 Carers (Recognition and Services) Act, from April 1996 carers also have the right to ask for their needs to be assessed separately. You can find the telephone number of your local social services department under the name of your county council. In London, it is listed under the borough council, and in large towns under your city or metropolitan council. In Scotland look for 'social work' under listings for your regional council. In Northern Ireland, help is given through local health and social services boards or trusts.

An interview will then be conducted to establish which services you and your parent require. A report, called a Care Plan, is then written up and you are entitled to the services listed in it. Your social services department then has a legal obligation to arrange for those services to be supplied, regardless of whether they lack funds or available places. It is a good idea, before the assessment, to make a list of the services you feel you need. Although your assessment is free, the council is at liberty to make a charge for the help it provides. You cannot be asked, as a carer, to meet the cost of services, and neither should charges cause hardship to your parent. The level at which fees are set can be challenged if felt to be unreasonable.

Your Care Plan will give details of how your situation is to be monitored and reviewed; it will also give the name of a contact person – your care co-ordinator or care-manager – with whom you can liaise over changes that arise. Particularly in these relatively early days of the new system, problems are emerging. Sometimes a person is refused an assessment without an explanation. There can be long delays between requesting and receiving an assessment, or between the assessment and receiving services. It can even be that a social services department decides not to give a service to a person assessed as needing it.

If you are unhappy with the treatment you receive, there are processes for registering complaints. If informal complaints prove ineffective, your next step is to complain in writing, in which case your social services department must respond within 28 days with a written decision. Failing this, you can ask for your grievance to be put before a Complaints Review Panel, consisting of three people, one of whom must be independent; they will make a recommendation to the director of social services. At this stage, you are entitled to the help of an advocate – a volunteer who speaks on behalf of recipients of community care. There are other complaints procedures open to you, including contacting the local authority's monitoring officer, or the ombudsman who investigates complaints against your local authority.

The Carers National Association have useful leaflets explaining clearly the system of community care, and how to request an assessment or lodge a complaint. They also operate a phone service called CarersLine (on 0171 490 8898) which is able to handle specific enquiries. It is as well to be armed with the facts before setting out on the road to organizing help.

Although social services departments have the lead role in assessing needs and organizing services, they are only one among a number of organizations likely to be providing the services arranged on your behalf. They do have some services for which they are responsible, but they also draw upon the health service and a range of independent organizations in designing packages of care. Indeed, the intention of the 1990 National Health Service and Community Care Act was that social services departments should gradually relinquish their role as direct providers of care, instead playing a role of organizing help. This has meant, for example, that we have seen local authorities selling many of their residéntial homes, and giving way to private companies and voluntary organizations as the primary suppliers of care. Local authorities have therefore had to develop systems for registering and inspecting private and voluntary homes. They also have no small control over the independent organizations who contract to supply services on their behalf. These groups fear the termination of their contract should they fail to please the local authority with which they are in partnership.

Assessments might appear the easiest route in securing help – though there is no reason why you, as a carer, cannot make private arrangements with companies supplying help. If you can afford it, you can contact directly agencies offering domiciliary support or private nursing care. You can also reach an independent agreement to have respite care from a private nursing home.

To help you prepare for an assessment, it is sensible to think through some of the options which might be available. The status of 'carer' may be so new to you that you may have little awareness of the sorts of services available. Try and think ahead, imagining which type of support will be of greatest, most strategic value (for example, a regular afternoon's break, the occasional week away from your responsibilities, or help with the practical tasks of caring). Then, when you receive an assessment, you can make a strong case for an appropriate package of services. One thing worth bearing in mind is that the range and extent of services offered vary greatly across the country. You will become particularly aware of this if you move house. Don't assume that, because a service is provided in one area, it will automatically be available elsewhere.

Information and advice

Perhaps your very first area of need will be for information about your parent's illness or disability. You will be eager for details of diagnosis and prognosis (the likely course or outcome of the condition). You will want to know how best to care for them. You may require new skills, particularly in the area of lifting a disabled person. You may also need legal and financial advice.

The most obvious source of this type of help is your GP. At this point, it is worth mentioning the varied experiences carers have of their GPs. Some speak highly of their family doctor, but others feel let down. Like social workers, GPs are described as 'gatekeepers', able to unlock the door to help for carers. They can fulfil a critical role in initially enabling someone to understand that they now have an official title, that of 'carer'. They can point them in the direction of the support which is their entitlement, in terms of state benefits and welfare services. Sadly, many fail in this function, focusing narrowly on medical needs. It is, nonetheless, vital that you press your GP for as much relevant information on your relative's condition as you are able, if necessary jotting down notes to aid memory, or tape-recording your conversation. The same goes for any encounters with specialists with whom your parent is in contact. Accurate facts are critical tools in your role as carer. They also help you to plan wisely, and to anticipate decline in your parent's health.

The medical profession is not the only source of helpful information, though. In particular, there are a good many charities which have been established to cater for sufferers and their relatives. Some are listed at the back of this book, but among the better known are the Alzheimer's Disease Society, Arthritis Care, CancerLink and the Parkinson's Disease Society. There are also general charities giving advice to older people and their carers, such as Age Concern, Help the Aged, and Counsel and Care.

On matters specifically about caring, you would be wise to contact the Carers National Association which gives information over the phone, and has pamphlets, many of which are free of charge. For a small annual fee you can become a member, and receive their regular newsletter which contains invaluable information. No doubt the assessment process itself will be enlightening, drawing to your attention details of which you were unaware.

Finally, there may be local initiatives to help carers in your area find information. There are the local branches of groups like Age Concern and the Carers National Association – and in many areas, local guides to services have been produced, for instance by the local Council for Voluntary Service. These guides are free and, though they are difficult to keep up-dated, they are invaluable, having an exhaustive list of the organizations providing support to disabled people and their carers. The Princess Royal Trust for Carers is in the process of setting up Carers

Centres across the country. Many are set up as High Street shops, so that carers can pop in for support and information, perhaps while out shopping. There may be a centre in your town.

Breaks from caring

The opportunity to take a break from caring is likely to be high on your list of priorities. The prospect of being responsible for care 24 hours a day, seven days a week, is unlikely to fill you with delight.

Taking a break from caring, or 'respite care' as it is known, comes in many guises. Short-term breaks of a few hours can be offered by a sitting service on a regular weekly basis. For example, a night-sitting service might offer a regular night's break. Or your respite may take the form of a longer break, say of a week or fortnight every couple of months. You need to consider which you feel to be of the greatest priority to you.

Sitting services vary across the country, but perhaps the leading organization providing this sort of back-up to carers is Crossroads – one of the few organizations set up expressly to relieve carers. Crossroads runs care-attendant schemes, often with funding from local authorities. Their structure and policies vary across the country, with some schemes charging a little for a service which others are able to provide free. Some are aimed at people caring for relatives within a specific age-group. The aim of Crossroads is simple: to provide care attendants to take over a carer's role for a few hours, allowing them to have a rest. Some carers choose to go out, others enjoy the luxury of being free from responsibility in their home. Carers are the focus of the service provided by Crossroads, which often extends beyond caring for the disabled person and giving practical help in the home, to offering genuine friendship and support.

Many other sitting services exist, some run by voluntary groups, others by private companies. A typical arrangement is for them to supply a sitter for a couple of hours each week, perhaps for a small charge. Sitters are usually carefully selected and trained, though it is not uncommon for carers to have difficulty entrusting a relative to someone they do not know. It can be helpful, then, if the first few visits are spent building a relationship with the sitter. Also, schemes will usually be happy for you to request a change of sitter if you are not altogether confident, though a good co-ordinator will be able to make instinctively effective matches. Some sitting schemes give night-cover. The sitter stays overnight, allowing the carer to get a good night's sleep. For people who are constantly having to tend to their relative at night-time, the rest this offers can be invaluable.

Besides sitting services, you might like to consider respite care from other sources. If you go out to work during the day, you may be especially interested in day-centres. These provide a valuable social outlet for older people who can otherwise feel lonely and isolated while their carer is away. Often, transport to the day-centre is arranged, and other services, such as chiropody and occupational therapy, will frequently be available. Day-care support varies both according to the flexibility of the scheme and the needs and choice of the client. Some people pay daily visits, while others attend only once or twice a week. Lunch clubs can also be helpful. These are often run by voluntary groups and again can provide your parent with a useful focus and source of companionship.

Respite care for longer periods can be arranged, usually through the use of respite beds in hospitals and in nursing or residential homes. Some carers opt to alternate several weeks caring for their parent at home with a fortnight's respite care. The older person is likely to be charged for respite care in a home, either by a flat-rate charge or on a means-tested basis. You may feel that longer breaks of this kind will give you the strength necessary to care for your parent. Or perhaps you feel small breaks more frequently would suit you better. The Carers National Association have fact-sheets on arranging respite care and finding out about holidays.

Caring for a sick parent is not something reserved for people in middle age, as Mandy discovered. When she was in her mid-twenties, Mandy nursed her mother who died of Hodgkin's disease. Several years later, married to Robert and with two young children (Amy aged three, and William aged 14 months), Mandy's mother-in-law Rose died from lung cancer, diagnosed when it was beyond surgery. She was 55. It was an acutely stressful time for Mandy and Robert, because Rose's death coincided with them moving house.

In the days following Rose's death, Mandy went each day with the children to visit Robert's father, Frank. Then, one afternoon, when Frank had arranged to travel over to Mandy and the children, he never arrived. Mandy rushed over to his house to find that he had collapsed against the front door. Unable to get into the house, Mandy waited anxiously for an ambulance while little Amy managed to hold on to her grandfather's hand through the letter box and talk to him. The children went with Mandy in the ambulance to the hospital, where it was discovered that Frank had had a massive stroke.

There followed several months of rehabilitation in hospital, during which time Mandy prepared for Frank to move to the family home. She feels sure that the knowledge he was to return to his family provided the key to Frank surviving that stroke. There was never any doubt in Mandy's mind that she would be able to cope with caring for two young children and a severely disabled parent. Looking back now, she wonders how she ever managed – though she is convinced that she would choose to do the same again. When she first had Frank at home, he was blind, incontinent, and unable to walk or speak. Mandy had no idea how to find help or the specialist equipment she needed. It was through the children's health visitor that she found out about useful aids. Frank's occupational therapist played a vital role too in supporting Mandy, showing understanding and kindness.

Otherwise, Mandy coped more or less single-handed. Occasionally friends would help by looking after either Frank or the two children, but no one felt confident enough to look after all three, so that Mandy could have a proper break. Only Mandy's own Dad, Jack, who was a good friend of Frank's, gave the family the occasional week's break, having Frank to stay with him.

It was the quality of Mandy's relationship with Frank that allowed her to continue for as long as she did. He was like a second father to her. She appreciated his gentleness, kindness and wonderful sense of humour. It thrilled her to see him reading stories to the children. He so obviously thrived in their company. After three or four years, however, Mandy's health broke down. The Ménière's disease she had had for some time worsened, and she eventually caught double pneumonia. It was clear that she could no longer continue to care for Frank at home, so Robert began to search for a nursing home which would satisfy their requirements. Frank spent two years in the home before his death in 1991.

In many ways, Mandy and Robert are still counting the cost of caring for Frank. In purely financial terms, the cost of topping up his nursing home fees almost ruined them. Their marriage faced extreme pressure as Robert resented the strain which the care of his father was putting on Mandy's health. Although he loved his father, their relationship had been a complicated one. His father's inability to handle finances had caused his mother endless worry, and now he could see his wife struggling too. He felt very guilty.

Perhaps of most concern to Mandy and Robert, though, is the long-term effect which caring for Frank appears to have had on William, now 11. Amy remembers only positive aspects of having her grandfather in the family home, but William was clearly affected by the stress it entailed. One manifestation is that he has difficulties sleeping, and goes into Mandy and Robert's bedroom each night as if to check they are still there. He was only four when Frank went into the nursing home, and was very angry with Mandy, feeling she had sent his grandfather away, and fearing the same might happen to him if he proved to be too much work. He is receiving counselling which is helping him work through his memories.

As for Mandy, she is putting her experience of caring to good use. She works part-time co-ordinating a voluntary scheme which gives respite to carers. She arranges for sitters to be with elderly people while their relatives take a break for a couple of hours. She is able to understand the needs of the carers she meets, and derives tremendous satisfaction from arranging support for them.

Practical help

You may feel overwhelmed by the sheer volume of work you now face as a carer. Particularly if you yourself are older, or in poor health, the kind of support you would prefer might be of a practical nature. In that case, you might like to enquire about receiving home care, or home help. Social services could arrange for someone to help with cooking, shopping, or personal tasks like dressing. Home-helps are less involved in cleaning people's homes these days, but their help is praised by many older people and their carers. According to your level of need, social services can arrange for a home-help or home-carer to visit regularly and help out.

Alternatively, Meals on Wheels may be of assistance – particularly if you are a carer who does not live with your parent, but worries that they are not cooking adequate meals. Again, you may find there is a charge for these practical services.

Help with nursing care

If you are finding aspects of nursing your parent difficult, the health service may be able to supply a district nurse once or twice a week for an hour or so. The nurse can give advice, and help with pressure sores, changing dressings and giving injections. More extensive nursing support may be available, say if you are looking after a terminally-ill cancer patient. Macmillan nurses, for instance, will gradually step-up the care they give to families in this situation, enabling the dying person to remain at home as long as possible.

You may find that the health authority in your area gives specialist medical advice to carers too. The continence advisory service can be of tremendous support. Sometimes courses on lifting skills are also available for carers. For those whose parents have mental health difficulties, a community psychiatric nurse may be able to offer support and advice.

Financial and legal help

Many carers claim that their biggest worry is over money. Often carers have to give up work, or reduce the hours they work, in order to care. This loss of income may come at a time when costs are rising; for instance, many households with disabled members have high fuel bills, due to the need to maintain a constant temperature, and because of the extra washing caused by such things as incontinence.

Many carers are unaware of the state benefits to which they and their parent are entitled. If your parent is under 65, they may be entitled to Disability Living Allowance. This benefit has two components:

- A component to cover personal care needs, which is payable at three rates depending on the level of a person's disability.
- A mobility component, which comes at two levels.

Unfortunately, if your parent is over 65, they cannot receive help with mobility costs. The Attendance Allowance which they are able to claim, however, is available at the higher and middle rates of the equivalent care component of the Disability Living Allowance.

If your parent receives the Disability Living Allowance or Attendance Allowance at the middle or higher rate, and if you are under 65 yourself and are caring for at least 35 hours a week, you may be entitled to the benefit specifically for carers, called the Invalid Care Allowance. This allowance is designed specifically as an earnings replacement benefit, so you are not entitled to it if already receiving Incapacity Benefit.

Those on low incomes can receive Income Support if working less than 16 hours a week, and receiving inadequate income from other sources. For instance, many pensioners who rely only on the state retirement pension qualify for Income Support. Carers on Income Support have a Carer Premium added to their benefit. Other benefits may be available to meet your financial needs:

- you may be entitled to a reduction in your council tax bill;
- you may qualify for Road Tax Exemption;
- you may be able to claim Housing Benefit;

- if you are on Income Support, you may be able to raise a lump-sum through applying for a Community Care Grant.

The area of financial planning for disability and caring is a minefield. It is unwise ever to accept advice from a lay-person over which benefits to claim. Your situation is unique, and requires the guidance of a specialist advisor for your income to be maximized. Social services may have a benefits advice agency to which you could turn, or you could enlist the services of your local Citizens' Advice Bureau. It may also be helpful to contact the Carers National Association's CarersLine (on 0171 490 8898). The Carers National Association has a useful range of free information sheets detailing the scope of available benefits, and touching upon other financial matters.

A further area of financial and legal anxiety for you may be the increasing need to take over the running of your parent's financial affairs, either because they are no longer able to get out, or because mental disorder has rendered them incapable. You may need to become their appointee in claiming social security benefits. If your parent has income from sources other than the state, you may need to take on a power of attorney, giving you legal control over their money. If you establish an enduring power of attorney, you will be able to continue to handle their affairs if and when they become mentally incapable. If you are having to set about making arrangements only after your parent has become mentally incapable, you will need to apply to the Court of Protection, if living in England or Wales. In Ireland and Scotland, the system differs slightly. Again, for advice or information, contact the Carers National Association or your Citizens' Advice Bureau.

Charitable trusts are a source of financial help of which many carers are unaware. Many trusts exist to give discretionary grants to individuals in need, particularly older people who have fallen on hard times. They can offer lump-sum grants, for example, for pieces of equipment or for holidays, or provide a small weekly allowance. Some give vouchers for food or clothes. Some trusts give to people according to their past occupational backgrounds, while others are linked to specific disabilities – but many are more general in remit. Most local libraries and advice centres hold books giving details of grants for people in need. Often, though, a third party would have to approach a trust-fund on your behalf. Some ask for applications from social workers; many will accept them from advice centres.

Aids, equipment and adaptations

Having appropriate equipment can make a world of difference in caring for a disabled person. You may be able to save yourself considerable effort and strain by finding out about the best types of equipment available. In addition, you may be able to add to your parent's independence. Specialist beds are available. Hoists can be fitted. Chair lifts can enable a person to manage stairs. Other smaller items can help a disabled person with eating or dressing.

Many items are available free, or for a small charge, from health authorities and local authorities – and a number of grants are also available. You can also buy privately, by mail-order or from show-rooms. Grants from the Social Fund may help with the cost of equipment. For more extensive adaptations to your home, Renovation Grants are available. You can also receive smaller Minor Works Grants. Finally, Disabled Facilities Grants are also available to improve access both into and around a disabled person's home. Before making purchases, though, it is best to consult an occupational therapist on the best types of equipment. The Carers National Association and the Royal Association for Disability and Rehabilitation may also be able to advise you on adaptations and equipment.

Friendship and counselling

Finally, as a carer, your chief need may be for support in handling painful feelings. We will consider sources of such help in subsequent chapters. It is appropriate now, however, to mention the existence of a network of self-help groups for carers, usually called carers support groups. Many are affiliated to the Carers National Association. Their function is to create an environment in which carers can talk about their feelings with people who understand, and discuss together ways of coping. Another route towards gaining emotional support is to employ the services of a counsellor, perhaps through the National Health Service or through voluntary or charitable groups such as CRUSE (bereavement counselling) and RELATE (relationship counselling). Many carers find counselling of tremendous value in resolving dilemmas and handling painful feelings.

Help for minority ethnic carers

Caring as someone from a different country of origin can be difficult. You may feel that the services provided are insensitive to your special cultural needs. You may have difficulty finding the help you need because of language barriers. The extent of sensitivity to cultural difference varies greatly across the country. Areas with a rich ethnic mix have become skilled in providing help sensitively to people from other cultures. On the other hand, you may find that little respect is shown for your cultural values.

At the very least, social services have a responsibility to offer you the services of a translator in the process of assessment. Try to secure the documents they supply in your mother tongue, as well as English. Ask about services geared especially to ethnic minority elders, such as day-centres which offer special diets and observe cultural and religious practices. Try not to let cultural objections stop you from benefiting from services which could lighten your load. If you have sufficient energy, invest your frustration in campaigning for greater adequacy in services provided for people from minority ethnic backgrounds.

Conclusion

Try to overcome your reservations over receiving help in your caring role. Your claim upon the various services on offer is perfectly legitimate. Caring unaided for any length of time is rarely feasible and can be counter-productive. Families do not always find that the support available is exactly to their liking. It nevertheless makes a world of difference to a situation which can threaten to become overwhelming.

4

Coping with relationships

Relating to your parent

Sarah felt herself to be trapped in her caring situation. She lived with her mother and, having been made redundant at the age of 53 with little prospect of finding another job, the alternative to caring was poverty and homelessness. She feared that, in the event of her mum moving to a nursing home, the roof would be sold from over her and there would be nowhere for her to live.

That was back in 1980. Sarah's mum, Violet, was in her early 80s. Her eyesight was rapidly diminishing and she was becoming increasingly frail. Sarah noticed that her mum's declining vision seemed to be accompanied by an increase in her demands. She became more bad-tempered with Sarah, even accusing her of being lazy when she was unable to maintain her housekeeping contributions after losing her job.

In 1985 Sarah was taken ill with pulmonary embolism. For the duration of Sarah's illness, her sister, a widow, cared for Violet in her own home. Afterwards Sarah's sister swore that she would never do so again, as she had found Violet maddeningly manipulative and difficult. That was the only help Sarah received from relatives, beyond visits lasting a couple of hours. Never once did anyone offer to sit with Violet to give Sarah a break. Even now, a year after Violet's death, Sarah feels very sore about the lack of support given by her brothers and sister, and what she believes to be their mercenary preoccupation with their inheritance. On more than one previous occasion, they have seemed willing to reduce Sarah to financial straits to gain access to their mother's capital, despite the fact that, unlike her, they all own property.

Violet resisted respite care, preferring the familiarity of her routine at home, but because of her poor health, it became essential for Sarah to arrange with social services for her mum to spend occasional weeks in a nursing home. Other than these welcome breaks, Sarah had little help. A home-help visited for two hours a week, and Sarah was also thankful for the contribution made by a Crossroads care attendant who sat with Violet each Wednesday evening. As Sarah's health deteriorated, she employed the services of a bath-nurse once a week.

There were many occasions when Sarah felt hurt and upset over things Violet had said to her, but her Christian faith kept her going and she was able to talk about her feelings with friends from church. Violet was 96 when she died in 1994. Her death was followed by a bout of serious heart trouble and a nervous breakdown for Sarah. In her late 60s, she felt that much of her life had passed her by while she was caring for her mum. Now, though, she feels more positive, ready to make a fresh start. Her mum belongs to the past. Only memories and an abundance of photographs remain. As she recovers from her latest illness, she looks forward to what the future may hold.

The quality of your relationship with your parent is likely to be the single most influential factor affecting your experience of caring. Caring, after all, is about a relationship. If that relationship holds warmth, affection and mutual respect, its strengths have the potential to make bearable the many trials likely to be encountered. On the other hand, if the central relationship is built on conflict, misunderstanding and resentment, the situation will remain tolerable only for a short period.

Let's stop for a moment to consider the complexities of our adult relationships with our parents. In many ways, caring for an elderly parent is more challenging than looking after a disabled partner or a child, for example. It is true that the sense of duty and obligation we feel can be equally strong, but the history of the relationship may make it more tricky. If one of our children becomes ill or disabled, the care we give them represents a continuation of our existing role. Similarly, if a partner needs our help, we are likely to share a pre-existing intimacy with them which makes caring seem a natural response. We have an equal relationship with them, and they are our chosen companion.

Parents are different. Part of becoming an adult is about breaking free from parental control and setting out on a different track. The experiences of adult life may have built a wall between us and them. Our life-styles and values may differ greatly. We may have lived many miles away from them, or deliberately avoided contact. Parents can also remind us of ourselves to an uncomfortable extent. Perhaps watching them is like looking in a mirror and seeing all our least attractive features. Or perhaps it seems to us that they represent what we may some day become. Often the clash of personality which occurs between parent and child is a product of similarities in temperament. There can also be the danger that you remind your parent of characteristics of your other parent to which they objected.

There is also the possibility that we harbour resentments towards our parents. We may feel that they have never properly understood or accepted us for who we are. We may have considered them to be harsh, overbearing, or interfering. Perhaps we even experienced neglect or cruelty at their hands. We may remember childhood hurt over a parental divorce or separation, and have memories of uneasy relationships with step-parents.

Relationships with parents have a long and rich history. They are rarely straightforward. To be thrust into an intimate, caring relationship with a parent who seems like a stranger can, therefore, be deeply uncomfortable and, indeed, is best avoided in some cases. We are not a society which tends to favour households of several generations. Older people have as much wish to live independently as their children. This may not apply in the case of families from minority ethnic groups, which traditionally have stronger extended families. But there is evidence that even families from these communities are experiencing the pressure of living in a society like ours, which is highly individualistic.

The relationship with in-laws is different again. Many people feel closer to their partners' parents than their own, but for others there can be memories of hostility and lack of acceptance when they first joined the family. Maybe too an in-law feels like a stranger, someone to whom you have never been close. Or you could be hampered in your caring role by a long-standing friction between your partner and their parent, and feel caught between their disagreements.

The common history you share with your own parents helps you to understand their approach to life. A parent-in-law may hold what seem to you alien views, and their life-style and priorities may be incomprehensible. Your own parents have helped to shape the way you are – but your parents-in-law come from a background which may be in sharp contrast to your own. This can generate frustration, tension and bewilderment.

It is to the credit of carers and their elderly parents that most caring relationships are based on feelings of affection. The most common experience is unsurprisingly a mixed one. While carers feel compelled to look after their parent, they still experience tension and frustration in their relationship. Nevertheless, many carers welcome the opportunity to be close to a parent in their final years. They take pride and delight in the task of making sure their parent is as comfortable and contented as possible. They are truly grateful to be able to repay a little of the kindness they have been shown from infancy by their parents.

Here are some of the changes in their relationship with their parent which carers find difficult.

'She isn't the mum she was'

In many ways this remark is self-evident. You would not be caring for your parent if something about them had not changed. However, the onset of frailty and disability can have a number of different effects. You may feel that, despite their disability, your parent is still the same person – their character and personality have not altered. On the other hand, you may be painfully aware of the effect of your parent's illness on their mind. This will be especially true if they have dementia or Alzheimer's disease. Communication becomes a terrible struggle. Many carers looking after dementia sufferers speak of the multiple losses they face. It can feel that their loved one has died while they are still living, because so little of their old self remains.

There are aspects of dementia, and indeed of several conditions affecting the brain, which are particularly painful for you as a carer to witness. Paranoia can emerge, with your parent accusing you of wanting to harm them. Then there is the possibility that your relative may even be violent and verbally aggressive towards you and other relatives. These things are totally out of character, and must be attributed to your parent's condition. It can be quite unnerving to hear a parent who has never sworn using language which makes your hair stand on end.

The ultimate insult of a condition like dementia is the possibility that the sufferer will eventually lose the ability to recognize loved ones. This represents the greatest challenge in your relationship with your parent, and can be deeply painful.

Other aspects of disability can appear to alter your parent's personality. There can be the frustration of coming to terms with limitations which disability imposes. This may manifest itself in bad temper. There can be the impact of continual pain, which tends necessarily to deplete a person's reserves of patience. And, perhaps again understandably, there is the sense of bitterness and resentment over suffering, or the failure to come to terms with the realities of old age. All these feelings can lead eventually to clinical depression. It is wise to be aware of the possibility of depression, a condition often overlooked in older people – though frequently experienced. If your parent has fallen into depression, it may be that treatment is available which can successfully alleviate the symptoms. Don't assume depression to be inevitable in old age.

Another factor which may dramatically alter your parent's personality is bereavement. For many older people, the loss of a lifetime's companion can be devastating. Having relied so heavily on a husband or wife over decades of marriage, it is not surprising that they fall apart and lose their will to live when the person dies. It is upsetting to have to handle your parent's anguish when you too are grieving the loss of a parent.

Finally, at this point it is wise to mention the effects on personality of many prescribed drugs. For instance, drugs prescribed for Parkinson's disease are known to affect personality. You would be well-advised to discover as much as possible about your parent's medication, so as to grasp as fully as possible the range of side-effects it might have.

Understanding the reasons for changes in your parent may help you to cope better with the sadness and frustration these can cause. It would be unrealistic to believe that your relationship with your parent could stay the same. Adjustments will be needed. All being well, though, a new equilibrium can be found. Through talking with other carers you may also learn techniques for communicating better with, say, a dementia-sufferer or someone who has had a stroke. Persevere and try, whenever possible, not to blame you parent for the consequences of their disability on their communication skills. Remember that words are not the only way to communicate. In wonderful ways, you can use touch and physical affection to convey love and reassurance.

'I feel like we've swapped places'

Caring for a disabled parent can feel somehow wrong. The dynamic of the relationship is upset. An imbalance is introduced. The roles are reversed.

We have an instinctive reflex which causes us to turn to our parents (if they have been reasonable parents) whenever we find ourselves in difficulty. Childhood teaches us to expect them to be there for us far more that we are there for them. True, as we grow older we become aware that they also need us, but generally we assume that their role in life is to respond to us. They help to get us established in our careers. They provide support when we have our own children. They represent a steady, dependable presence.

It can come as a shock, therefore, to find that in later life our parents are turning increasingly to us for help. Something inside causes us to react against the notion that we should take responsibility for them. Their pride, too, presents an obstacle. It is only with reluctance that they accept support from a person whom they have taken pride in having nurtured. It is particularly difficult to have to offer personal care to a parent; it can seem to destroy totally any last vestiges of dignity they have. Helping a person with toileting, when that person was the one who taught you to use the toilet, can be upsetting.

Some carers feel sad that they can no longer share their troubles with their parent, who seems now completely preoccupied with their own worries. They find it difficult to think of any ways in which their parent still gives to them. The relationship can seem one-sided. Only memories of earlier love they received helps such carers cope with the inequality which now exists in the relationship. Relationships function best when there is give and take. In the absence of this reciprocity, a relationship can be placed under great strain.

'He never treated me like an adult'

The reversal of roles between carers and their elderly parents can be complicated yet further by the parent's refusal to acknowledge their child as an independent adult. Even while the roles are being swapped, the parent continues to exercise control over the child. If your parent has always been domineering, never respected your judgement or decisions, it can be difficult to care for them with a good grace. You may even fear their disapproval and feel that you are treading on eggshells lest you offend them in some way.

If would be far easier, you may think, if your parent had been able to accept you as an independent adult and treated you accordingly.

'If only she would be more co-operative'

Hand-in-hand with the tendency to control their children, comes a reluctance in dominant parents to co-operate. Some carers are driven mad by their parent's stubborn refusal to accept outside help, to adhere to a treatment regime, to have respite care . . . An unco-operative parent can make caring seem like a perpetual battlefield. As a carer, you know you have no absolute right to impose care on your parent, but must tolerate their obstinacy. This entails an assault on your self-esteem which may affect you badly.

Looking back on her childhood, Alice remembers trying to behave well, but being chastised over small failures. However, old photos show that she looked a very happy child. As an only child, though, she later experienced the full weight of parental aspiration, and felt pressurized over the decisions she made at key stages in her life.

Later, as a mother herself, Alice found visits from her own mother,

Mary, upsetting and difficult. She felt Mary interfered and offered little support. When Mary was widowed she remained living in the town where she had spent much of her married life. Alice and her husband, George, lived a considerable distance away, so it was Mary's neighbours who helped her as she became frail. By the time she reached her mid 80s, though, Mary's neighbours were no longer able to offer the back-up she needed. Alice's daughters, Kate and Sarah, were both doctors, and advised that their grandmother be encouraged to move to the town where Alice and George were living.

The move was a big step for Mary, but she knew the area well. The thought of being closer to her grandchildren and great-grandchildren appealed to her. So, at 86, she organized her affairs and cheerfully moved to a flat down the road from her daughter's home. The arrangement was that Mary would visit for lunch some days. Alice also took her mum out in the car wherever she went.

Difficulties soon arose. First of all, Alice's friends were keen to befriend Mary. They would arrange to call on her, but Mary did not make a note of the time they were to arrive and would not be home. Eventually people stopped trying. Alice remembers feeling mortified to hear her mum then complain in public that local people were unfriendly compared with the folk in her old town.

Alice herself suffered from exhaustion. After spending several hours each morning engaged in home-based voluntary work, she would need a rest after lunch. She found her mum unsympathetic to her needs and determined to call when she was sleeping. Mary refused to allow Alice to have her flat cleaned, and stubbornly resisted wearing the bandages needed for her leg ulcers. And yet there were times when Mary would express appreciation, and Alice heard from friends that her mum praised her warmly in their company, though complaining also occasionally. The times when Mary was particularly ill were different. Alice would stay in the flat with her and found that she was more obliging and willing to co-operate then. Otherwise, when Mary was put out, she would make scathing comments which painfully reminded Alice of similar destructive remarks which had damaged her confidence as she was growing up.

There was a great temptation for Alice to bully her mum, now that she had the upper hand. The sheer exhaustion and frustration of the situation caused her to lose her temper. She remembers with shame one occasion when she slapped her mum, albeit after extreme provocation. Indeed, even George, by nature very patient, found himself becoming angry with Mary.

George retired a couple of years after Mary moved to the flat, and was also closely involved in caring for her. Eventually Mary's health so deteriorated that she moved to a nursing home mid-way between the homes of Alice and George and their daughters. For the final six months of her life, then, Mary was cared for in an environment of which Alice speaks highly. Staff welcomed Mary's many guests, and Mary seemed proud to be surrounded by such a large, supportive family. She died at the age of 91.

It is two years since Mary's death, but Alice still has difficulty forgiving herself for the lack of patience she exercised during the five years of caring. She finds it difficult to recall Mary's intransigence and unpleasantness which drove her to distraction. She has a longing to start afresh and discover new reserves of tolerance and kindness, but accepts that she would act no differently a second time round. Fundamentally, she acknowledges that the constant friction over minor things was the result of similarities in personality. Like her mum, she was uptight and tense. Alice had no difficulty giving practical help, but it irked her that her relationship with her mum never became one of adult to adult. When she became an adult, she felt Mary continued to treat her as a child. Then, towards the end, Alice herself took on the parental role while her mum reverted to the child.

Alice has a deep desire to help other carers. If asked for advice, she says she would encourage people in a caring role like hers to try and dwell on their mother's good points and not their faults. She would suggest that they remember that their mother is old, and that being old can be not much fun. She recommends trying to act pleasant even when you feel hostile and angry; she found that after a while she would actually start to feel pleasant. Finally, she would like to point out to other carers the danger that they might feel quite differently about their situation when it is too late to put things right.

'All I want is a little appreciation'

Unco-operative parents may be those who also express little gratitude towards their carers. How disheartened you feel as a carer to be giving so much of yourself and receiving no thanks in return. 'Thank you' really is a magic phrase. To hear it said can make daily strains and pressures easier to bear. To sense that your parent is interested in your life, and cares about the things that bother you, can be a big help. To know that they understand the difficulties involved in caring and feel appreciative towards you can make all the difference.

It can be difficult to understand why your parent does not offer the thanks you feel is owing to you. Their lack of expressed gratitude may be brought about by a sense of shame that they are having to rely so heavily upon you. It may be caused by hurt pride. Perhaps also it is the result of denial; they feel better for pretending you actually do little for them. Or they may genuinely feel that you owe it to them to be there for them in their hour of need.

The difficulty with gratitude is that it has to be spontaneous. It only means something if unprompted. If you are prepared to wait, however, you may find your patience rewarded. Many parents wait until they are near death before they acknowledge the care and concern their child has given, and how important it has been to them. Saddest of all is the possibility that your parent saves their praise for another person. They tell everyone how wonderful you are – except you.

'She lives her life through me'

If having a parent who is fiercely independent and refuses help at every turn is difficult to handle, so is having a parent who becomes totally dependent on you. You can feel under dreadful pressure if your parent has little life outside their relationship with you. Frailty in old age can leave a person very isolated. If housebound, an elderly person relies on visitors. Friends may cease to come, and yours may be the only regular face they see. There is also the possibility that they have alienated friends and relatives, or not bothered to keep in touch, knowing you will always be there for them.

Your parent may become skilled in inducing guilt. They may be capable of finding a whole host of reasons why you should not leave them. They are jealous of the time you spend away, asking you to account for every minute. They may resent your friendships and begrudge the time you spend with other relatives. Naturally, you don't enjoy thinking of them feeling lonely, so there is the pressure to spend less and less time away.

It may be that your parent's dependency is of a more practical kind. They refuse to perform tasks of which you know they are capable, preferring to let you do them. Or they seem unable any longer to make decisions: you find yourself making even the tiniest of choices – such as what to wear or eat – on their behalf. You feel you must create activity to fill their day, as they lack the impetus to pursue their own interests. Their conversation becomes limited, as there is so little upon which they can focus their thoughts. Carers in this situation can find themselves feeling smothered, longing to break free of the all-pervasive presence and influence of their parent. It is a trial to sense that a person's well-being rests entirely on your shoulders, that they literally draw their energy for life each day from you.

'I was never the daughter-in-law she wanted'

It may be that you are caring for a parent-in-law whom you feel has never truly welcomed you into the family. Perhaps you have struggled for years to conquer feelings of insecurity and inadequacy over your role in your partner's family. Now, even in subtle ways, your parent-in-law continues to send out signals that you fail to fulfil their image of the perfect partner for their son or daughter. Your self-esteem is taking a battering, and resentment – or perhaps even hatred – are simmering inside you. Despite all your attempts to be accepted, you still feel an outsider, a disappointment, a failure. Offering genuine kindness and care is a seemingly impossible challenge.

Finding ways of coping

If you are beginning to sense that your relationship with your parent or parent-in-law is breaking down, it is time to seek change or help. Living in continual conflict and disharmony is helpful for neither of you. The atmosphere generated is likely to put you at risk of saying or doing things you may later regret bitterly. Many carers admit to appalling guilt over incidents where sheer rage and frustration drove them to shout at their parent, or even hit them. Far better to take measures to enable you to avoid this possibility.

Creating some distance

One strategy which reduces tensions in a caring relationship is to create some distance between the carer and their parent. Partly this entails ensuring that, to some degree, the two of you continue to live your lives separately, as you have for most of your adult life. This might mean, if you live in the same house, having parts of your home which belong to each of you, and resisting the temptation to be always in the same room. Partly, too, though, it means creating some emotional distance. It may seem harsh, but your very survival may depend upon becoming slightly impervious to excessive demands which your parent makes, and developing a thick skin when it comes to any techniques of manipulation. One study of daughters (Lewis and Meredith, 1988) described the danger of becoming totally immersed in caring, and completely at the dictates of a parent.

Having a break

A lifeline may well be those few hours a week when you are away from caring. A regular break to meet up with a friend, go swimming or pursue a hobby can help restore your sense of perspective. It can allow you to cultivate a more philosophical approach. There is always the danger that you will be reminded more forcefully on your return of the intense difficulty in your relationship, but all being well, a few hours' relaxation will provide the patience needed to persevere.

Having a go-between

Things may become so tense between you and your parent that it becomes advisable to draw in a third party who can help resolve conflict. If you feel you are achieving nothing through talking with your parent, it might be that another member of the family could be called upon as arbitrator, allowing you both to see the other's point of view. A professional person, such as your social worker or GP, might also be able to act as a go-between. The charity RELATE, whose local offices are listed in the phone directory, offers a valuable service to those going through relationship difficulties – not just those whose marriage or sexual relationships are in crisis.

Talking to a counsellor

A final strategy, which many carers have found to be extremely beneficial, is to find a counsellor. It tends to be the carer who visits the counsellor alone, so the problem is only tackled from one side. It can contribute tremendously, though, to your understanding of the source of conflict with your parent. A counsellor can help you trace the pattern within your relationship with your parent, and find the origins of difficulties. They can then work with you towards discovering ways of coping. Your doctor may be able to refer you to a counsellor available on the NHS. Also, many voluntary and charitable organizations offer counselling; your local Citizens' Advice Bureau will help you find out about local groups.

Relating to friends and relatives

Caring can significantly affect other relationships, beyond the one between carer and elderly parent. Sometimes it may seem that you are being asked to make agonizing choices between the people you love. You may come to resent the fact that your parent absorbs precious time you might otherwise be able to spend with other loved ones. Or you may feel anger towards relatives who could be doing more.

Brothers and sisters

We noted in the previous chapter how common it is for carers to feel abandoned by brothers and sisters who could be helping. It is the legacy of a passing age that unmarried daughters are automatically assumed to be responsible for ageing parents. Regardless of their health or commitments elsewhere, many feel under pressure to take on the caring role and feel bitter towards siblings who hide behind their husbands, wives and children. Many single people feel they have more to lose in taking on a caring role. They fear that, having given up a job and lost touch with friends, they will have little life or income left when their parent dies. They argue that, in many ways, it would be easier for a married brother or sister to care, since they have other close family to support them.

Even when you take on the caring role gladly, and whatever your personal circumstances, you may still feel you have a right to expect help from brothers and sisters. You may argue that it is only fair that they do their bit to help. Many families do pull together effectively – though other carers find brothers or sisters who refuse the slightest involvement. Requests for a break can meet with flat refusal.

Even when your brothers or sisters fail to help, you may still find that your parent idolizes them, living for their occasional visits and refusing to find fault with them, while broadcasting your every deficiency. This is a cause of deep anger and resentment among carers. But the trouble with harbouring resentment towards family members, however justified, is that it achieves little. No amount of persuasion can force them to pull their weight. You need somehow to get the feelings off your chest, perhaps by confiding in a friend; accept that their help is unlikely, and seek the support you need from elsewhere.

Although Ethel found caring for her dad difficult, she says she would do it again. In fact, when he died last year at the age of 85, she felt angry with him for leaving her after she had committed so many years of her life to caring for him. Interestingly, though, she is adamant that she would not want her four children to care for her in her old age.

Ethel has been divorced twice. She fled nine years ago from the house she owned, because her second husband was physically and mentally cruel towards both Ethel and their son, the youngest of her four children. She requested a council house a few doors away from her dad's home, when she realized he needed help. Terry, Ethel's dad, had been widowed for many years. After living an active life, during which he worked as a miner, he was struggling to come to terms with the emphysema that was gradually confining him to his home. He bitterly regretted being unable any longer to look after his garden.

Terry had never been a man to make friendships and, of his three children, Ethel (the youngest) was the only one who was close enough emotionally to want to offer the support he needed. Ethel felt let down on many occasions by her elder brother and sister who visited their dad no more than a couple of times a year, though they lived in the same town. Unlike Ethel, they had space in their homes where Terry could stay. They also owned cars, something which Ethel could not afford. She wished they would take Terry out for trips, because his life had become so confined. On the one occasion Ethel was able to take a week's holiday, her brother and sister begrudged her request that they keep an eye on Terry. On her return, she was horrified to discover that Terry had received only one visit from her sister and none from her brother.

Ethel faced demands from many people. Raising four children alone was a challenge in itself, without the added pressure of running her dad's home – shopping, washing, cleaning, cooking . . . Help from outside organizations was minimal (just Meals on Wheels twice a week, and two home visits each week towards the end of her dad's life). Ethel believes her dad received so little outside help simply because she lived nearby.

Perhaps hardest of all were the emotional demands placed on Ethel by her dad. Terry was jealous of her time. He would create jobs to prevent her leaving, would insist on knowing where she was all the time, and bitterly resented any friendships or interests she struggled to cultivate. His demands escalated to such an extent that a row was inevitable. In some ways, Ethel regrets staying away for three days after the argument, but looking back she feels it helped Terry to understand the strain he was placing on her. She feels she was at risk of losing her identity completely. Despite all she did for Terry, she was not able to go to him for support, no matter how difficult her own situation. His illness prevented him from offering her help.

Counselling has helped Ethel to rebuild her life after losing her dad. She has a part-time job as supervisor in a local book shop. She is also enjoying a course to learn sign language, and is involved as a volunteer in a club for disabled people. At 46, she has a new sense of direction in life.

Partners

Taking on responsibility for an ailing parent can have profound ramifications on your relationship with your partner. Your time will cease to be your own, opportunities for shared leisure will be reduced, and your parent's demands may well conflict with your partner's wishes. The situation can become all the more tense if your parent comes to live in your home. This can really upset your relationship with your husband or wife. Much will depend on the nature of your parent's relationship with your partner. If there is a history of mutual respect and affection, tension will be less likely. If there has been distrust and dislike, however, you may be opting for a turbulent time.

You may quickly find yourself torn in two, asked to choose between two people whom you love. Resentments may develop on either side, as your parent and partner compete for your attention. One way of minimizing conflict is to make sure that your role in helping your parent has been negotiated from the start, with each party involved. It would be most unwise to invite your parent to live with you without first gaining your partner's consent. Your parent would feel an unwelcome guest, and your partner would have difficulty in accepting their presence. It may be necessary to find a compromise which, while suiting no one perfectly, avoids a situation which is deeply distasteful to one of you.

You need to resist attempts on your parent's part to come between you and your partner. They may even be unaware of the effects of their actions, which stem from insecurity and vulnerability. Be gentle but firm. Guard time with your partner as an investment in the future, as well as a source of strength in the present. If your partner knows that you will do nothing to jeopardize your relationship, they are more likely to be willing to give the practical and emotional support which could be the key to survival. If your partner is reluctant to endorse even a limited caring role for you, then it might be time to question your relationship. What kind of person will try to prevent you from showing kindness towards someone who means a great deal to you?

Tensions between you and your partner differ somewhat if you are caring for one of their parents. It is easy for you to resent the extra responsibilities you feel expected to accept. This is particularly true if you feel that your partner is not doing their share of the caring – perhaps because of outside commitments, or the view that caring is 'women's work'. You may also feel that your partner takes for granted what can feel a sacrificial commitment on your part to their parent's well-being. They show little gratitude – or even any insight into the stress you are under.

Caring for a parent or parent-in-law has been known to cause relationship or marriage breakdown. The strains and conflict can become intolerable if they are not addressed. Again, it may be advisable to call upon the services of RELATE (the relationship counselling charity, listed in local phone directories), if you and your partner have stumbled on intractable differences of opinion over the care each of you gives to your parent or parent-in-law.

Children and grandchildren

It can be a source of heartache for carers that their all-consuming caring role keeps them from spending time with children and grandchildren. Childhood is short, and you can feel time ebbing away. You may feel guilty over neglecting the children in the family. You may feel that their opportunities are circumscribed by your caring role. You are not free to take them to places, as you would like. Holidays are difficult to take. Quality time for reading and playing with them, or helping with homework, is a scarce commodity.

There is no escaping the fact that taking on responsibility for a parent does limit your potential to give in other areas. The decision involves real sacrifice. Many carers, however, feel there are compensations for children in being close to older relatives. Grandparents and great-grandparents can fulfil a unique role in listening to children and helping them grow. The children of carers, who take the risk of having a parent to live with them, often grow up with fond memories of their grandparent. The elderly person may act as a pivot within the extended family, holding it together. They hand down cherished family traditions and stories. They can be valuable mediators in conflicts between younger generations.

Many carers also value the advice of their elderly relatives, especially over matters of raising children. They turn to their mother or father, mother-in-law or father-in-law, for guidance over decisions and for comfort in trouble. The older person can be a steadying presence, a source of calm.

There may come a time when caring for your parent seems to have become detrimental to your children's well-being. We consider this eventuality in greater detail in Chapter 7. If alternative care has to be sought, there need be no severing of links between your parent and your family. The relationship is merely re-established on a new footing. Children and grandchildren can accompany you on visits to a residential or nursing home. They may even visit on their own, if old enough. Sometimes harsh decisions are unavoidable, and it can be difficult to escape feelings of guilt, but in time many carers come to realize that their decision was a wise one.

Friends

Friends can surprise us when we find ourselves in a caring situation. Many carers feel that this is the time when friends show their true colours. Friendships can become more difficult to sustain when you carry hefty caring duties. You no longer have the time or freedom to meet up when and where you please. There can be a greater onus on your friends to keep in touch. It may become necessary for them to visit you, which might entail a degree of effort.

Some carers cannot praise their friends enough. They report that friends have given practical support and been faithful in visiting, writing letters and making phone calls. Their concern and care has made a huge difference. Other carers, however, find themselves feeling disappointed over the apparent neglect of formerly close friends who don't make the effort to visit, and lose touch completely in come cases. Carers often then feel betrayed and resentful. (Carers may have similar feelings towards their parent's friends who never visit, knowing that their parent feels cut off and wishing that people would call on them.)

If you have done as much as you can to keep up with old friends, but to no avail, it might be worth looking for new contacts, perhaps among others in a similar situation. Many people find carers support groups a source of friendship. It can be a great release to spend time in the company of people who share your challenges and frustrations. The Carers National Association, or your local social services department, will help you find out about groups in your area.

Carers often become isolated without realizing it. They reach a point where they see very few people to speak to, and can claim hardly any good friends. To be cut off from social contact is hard to bear, and needs to be avoided if at all possible.

Conclusion

Investing time and energy in making other relationships work for you could well be the key to a fulfilling and rewarding caring relationship. If necessary, swallow your pride and be prepared to admit that things are not working well in your relationships and that you need help. There is no shame in admitting to friction in a situation which would try the saintliest of souls!

5
Managing feelings

In Chapter 4 we considered at length some of the feelings which can surround troubled relationships for carers. In this chapter, we will look more closely at the range of emotions which carers commonly experience.

First, though, it is important to remember that each of us is different. You may be able to identify with some of the feelings described here; on the other hand, you may have had none. Caring does not come with a job description specifying ideal characteristics. Some carers are emotionally stable, naturally calm and have a usefully thick skin. They are able to maintain their equilibrium whatever they face. Others, however, are volatile and easily swayed in their moods by circumstances they meet. Roller-coaster rides are by no means unfamiliar to carers; the extreme stress they face can cause them to swing from fulfilment to despair and back again very suddenly.

The feelings

The rewards

It might help to start by considering some of the positive aspects about caring for your parent, before moving to the less pleasant feelings. Almost every carer can find something good to say about caring. However hard it can sometimes become, some element of enjoyment or fulfilment helps them to carry on. Usually this is because, underlying their efforts, is a fund of love and affection towards their parent. You may not often tell them you care about them, but there is a deep-rooted understanding that the two of you are special to one another. Yes, you have had your fights and disagreements – but you have come through them all with your friendship intact.

Often carers speak of their wish to repay something of their parent's dedication throughout childhood and into their adult lives. It can be enormously enjoyable to feel that you are giving something in return for their years of sacrifice. Carers also derive great pleasure from making their parent happy. They look for lots of little ways to please them, to offer comfort and relief from pain. Many take a great pride in the excellence of the care they provide, drawing from it a sense of self-esteem.

Fundamentally there is something within us which derives meaning and purpose from caring for others. Some would say that women are brought up with an unfair dose of this nurture-drive, and need to be freed to a degree from its powers. There can, of course, be an unhealthy dependence on caring for others as a source of identity. But most carers find that, in some scarcely definable way, caring helps to bring motivation to their life. Having to consider your parent's needs helps to get you up in the morning, perhaps even offers a therapy enabling you to focus outwards, instead of on your own anxieties and troubles.

Through the years, I have marvelled at the selflessness and endurance of carers I have met – though many of them consider their own caring to be flawed. Caring can turn your world upside down, but it can also help you discover what really matters in life. It can draw from you qualities you never dreamed that you possessed. It can change your character for the better, and for ever. In truth, caring is one of those peculiar experiences brimming over with contradictions. Those who feel they have lost everything can strangely realize they have found a treasure of incalculable value. In our materialistic, individualistic world, it may not always be popular to say that relationships matter above all else – but carers prove, through their commitment, that this is indeed the case.

The grief

Feelings of grief and loss can often be associated with caring. The immediate source of sadness is your parent's declining health and independence. You long for them to be as you have always known them – fit and resourceful. It hurts to see them struggle over tasks they desperately want to continue to perform. You may find it hard to bear seeing them in pain, or suffering the humiliation imposed by so many of the diseases of old age. A stroke can, in a moment, rob someone of their ability to move and to communicate; what agony you suffer with them as they battle for a simple word or familiar name. Alzheimer's disease is a relentless process of deterioration, characterized frequently by a gripping sense of fear and anxiety. You long to comfort, but can do nothing, it seems, to relieve the effects of the illness. How many unseen tears are shed by carers over the ravages of illness and disability?

Not only may you grieve for the loss of your parent as they have always been, but you may also be pained by losses resulting from your decision to care for them. You may have given up your home to go and live with them. You may have left your job, and miss the companionship of colleagues. Other areas of your life may have been affected: hobbies, friendships, activities, commitments . . . You may feel, too, that your dreams have faded away. Hopes for the future have had to be put to one side, perhaps never to be retrieved. You may catch yourself thinking, 'If only I hadn't had to care for mum, I could have pursued that career I wanted, or found a partner I could love.' So there is the grief over missed potential and lost opportunities. The sensation of loss can be a hallmark of caring, and may continue long after your parent has died.

The frustration of feeling tied

Many carers speak of feeling imprisoned. They desperately miss the freedom to come and go as they please. Carers struggle especially with these limitations when they are at a stage of life at which they had anticipated being free at last – perhaps from the demands of raising children or from the rigours of a working life. Ironically, caring for an elderly parent most typically beckons at the very moment when children are leaving home and retirement is approaching.

You may feel that you are constantly watching the clock, in order to be home by the time your mother or father returns from day-centre. Or you may pine for the time when you were able to have nights out at your choosing. Perhaps it is simply the niggling feeling of worry and responsibility which will never leave you alone. If only you could be free from the anxiety.

Anger and resentment

Mingle among a group of carers and you will quickly discern that there is much which makes them angry. We have already noted in Chapter 4 that anger can be directed towards family-members. There can be annoyance over relatives who refuse to lend a hand. There can be irritation over attitudes and behaviours of the person being cared for: the refusal to co-operate; the excessive demands; the manipulation; the over-dependency. Sometimes irritation can turn to rage, and you find yourself shouting at your parent or administering a sharp slap which you then regret for days.

Anger can have wider causes, though. Sometimes carers feel enraged by the treatment they receive at the hands of the so-called caring agencies. They may feel doctors have failed to diagnose or treat their parent adequately. They may be incensed by the cold, off-hand manner in which they are addressed. They may feel that the system for obtaining support is hopelessly inefficient and haphazard. They may be outraged at the level of fees charged, or the length of waiting lists for treatment.

Sometimes it is a carer's employer who behaves insensitively, inviting their condemnation. Perhaps it might also be a carer's friends, social club or church that has let them down. The extreme degree of stress carers often endure can mean that they lose their tempers easily. Understandably, the anger they feel can be over the caring situation itself: 'Why did this have to happen to us?'; or 'It's not fair that we should have to go through this!'

Another shade of anger is resentment. As a carer you may feel hugely resentful towards members of your family, or towards professionals whom you feel have treated you badly. The danger is that anger and resentment begin to build up, and can have a damaging effect on your mental health. It is not good to live in a ferment of rage and bitterness, fuelled by every slight perceived affront. You alone suffer the long-term effects of these feelings. They need to be acknowledged, allowed an outlet and then left behind. You may never master them fully – but they should eventually lose some of their sting.

Loneliness

Carers' lives are often extremely confined. Apart from a few hours' respite care a week, they spend the vast majority of their time at home with their parent. Many find that friends of their own, and of their parent, gradually cease to visit. The phone no longer rings. They feel 'out of sight, out of mind'. Obvious sources of companionship, such as work, are gone. A profound degree of loneliness can then creep up on a carer. Before they realize it, they find that they are going for days on end without conversation with anyone outside their home.

In addition, some carers find that their parent offers little in the way of companionship, due to the nature of their disability. With no one with whom to share a stimulating, honest conversation, problems can quickly grow out of proportion. We each need social contact if we are to thrive. It cannot be healthy for a carer to become isolated and lonely. If you feel alone and in danger of becoming cut off, you probably need to take steps towards enlarging your social circle and making new friends.

At the age of 51, Pam lives with her father and sister, both of whom have relied upon her care since the death of her mother 12 years ago. Albert, Pam's father, has severe arthritis. He can manage to totter to the commode and get upstairs with help, but never leaves the house now. He is 88 and it is now 28 years since he retired from his career in banking. Pam feels close to her dad. They are alike in many ways – and the sense of humour Pam inherited from him is a critical factor in her ability to cope with the demands of caring. She does not begrudge in the least the care she gives her dad, even though she sometimes feels impatient over his growing frailty; he is appreciative and easy-going.

On the other hand, Pam does feel intense resentment towards her older sister, Ruth. Ruth has cerebral palsy in her right side and is epileptic. She also suffers the after-effects of an accident many years ago. As a child, Ruth had severe temper tantrums and her needs dominated family life. As a consequence, from the age of nine, Pam has suffered from depression. Partly to escape what she felt to be parental pressure to accept a lifelong responsibility for Ruth's care, Pam married in her 20s. The relationship proved disastrous: Pam was a battered wife and left her husband after only nine months of marriage.

The pain of her failed marriage left a deep mark on Pam. She had previously lived in flats of her own, but she no longer felt confident enough to live alone, and returned to her parents' home. Though she managed to develop a successful career, the marriage had left her vulnerable and she began to experience schizophrenic episodes. Eventually, five years after the break-up of her marriage, Pam's health collapsed and she was admitted to hospital. She was unable to return to work for a long time.

When her mum died, therefore, Pam took on the role of carer full-time. Caring for her dad presented little difficulty – but she has continued to battle with resentment towards Ruth, whom she feels is bitter towards her for being able-bodied. Ruth continues to be unpredictable in her moods and exacting in her demands on Pam. Pam frequently feels put down and belittled by Ruth, who makes few allowances for her sister's needs. Pam feels that Ruth could do much more at home, and is hurt that Ruth is secretive about her job at the skills centre, where she works as receptionist and telephonist three days a week.

Lately Pam has found life particularly taxing. Believing herself to be agoraphobic, she was surprised to discover that her problems stemmed from an over-speedy withdrawal from the drugs she had been taking for many years for her schizophrenia. Coping with caring for two relatives, while battling with anxiety, insomnia and nausea, has been difficult. She has badly needed the four week-long breaks which she is able to take each year. This respite is made possible by a combination of daily visits from social services, and the kind help of a friend who makes meals for Albert and Ruth. Pam felt let down several years ago when, because of spending cuts, the family's social worker lost his job and their case was closed.

Pam and Ruth's relationship is so tense and difficult that Pam feels it would be better for Ruth to find sheltered accommodation elsewhere. Unfortunately, Albert will not contemplate living away from Ruth, even though he understands Pam's difficulties. He vows that, while he lives, Ruth will have a home under his roof. And so, for as long as Pam feels compelled to care for her dad, she must also endure Ruth's incessant demands.

Pam feels isolated. Albert lives quietly, spending most of his time reading. Pam has occasional phone calls with friends, but wishes people came to visit and keep her company. She recognizes she cannot continue for much longer as a double-carer, and is looking into the possibility of finding a paid carer to help her look after Ruth. She dreams of one day having the freedom to be herself.

The guilt

Partly because of the anger which their circumstances can provoke, carers often wallow in an unhealthy sea of guilt. They feel nothing but remorse, and reproach themselves for the occasions when they lose their temper. They consider themselves very wicked to be capable of shouting at someone who is old and ill. It is ironic that the people who are doing most for their parents are the very ones who blame themselves for not doing enough. Carers somehow set themselves unreasonably high standards, and condemn themselves when they fail to reach them – as they inevitably will.

You need to banish from your mind, then, any thought that accepting help in your caring role is a sign of weakness and lack of devotion. You need to tell yourself that you are not perfect – and neither can you be expected to be. We each have mood swings. We all react differently under pressure. What counts is your genuine, underlying care and concern for your parent.

Depression

Depression tends to creep up as a result of accumulated stresses experienced through caring. The potent combination of feelings described above – grief, anger and guilt – if borne over a long period, can drive you into a trough of clinical depression. Everything seems dull and black, all colour and vibrancy gone. You are beset by overwhelming feelings of gloom and negativity. Your sleep becomes fitful, perhaps you lose your appetite. Life no longer seems worth living.

The worst thing is that no one seems to understand. They urge you to cheer up and snap out of it, because things are not that bad really. The trouble is, you find it impossible to look on the bright side any more. Laughter and smiles are hard to find, tears come quickly. You need to recognize this for what it is – an illness. It is not an inevitable, inescapable state of mind; nor is it failure. You could receive medication from your GP to help you regain your normal, healthy outlook. Don't live with depression when a cure could easily be found.

Exhaustion

Tiredness seems to be an occupational hazard for carers. Many have broken nights, perhaps caused by the incontinence or restlessness of their parent. Every waking hour is filled with jobs, many of which are strenuous and physically demanding. Carers whose time and energies are split many ways are particularly prone to exhaustion. Many are rushing to get loved ones breakfasted before dashing off for a full day's paid work, only to return in the evening for a further shift of caring. They tumble into bed late at night, completely stripped of every ounce of energy, aware that the instant they fall asleep the alarm will ring, beckoning them towards another such day.

Realistically, this life-style cannot be sustained indefinitely. The outcome can be that the carer's health collapses, requiring several weeks, even months, of complete rest. Unfortunately, carers assume that the desire to be available for everyone and everything needing their attention translates into the ability to achieve the impossible.

You need to be looking out for the danger signs. Are you susceptible to every infection that comes your way? Are your emotional responses starting to wear thin, with tantrums and tears featuring often? Do you feel like going back to bed as soon as you get up in the morning? Is concentration becoming a battle? Ask yourself if you are giving your body the rest it needs. You may pay heavily if you fail to observe its warnings.

Anxiety

Many aspects of life can become sources of worry for carers. Typically the most pressing concern can be over the person being cared for. Carers who do not live with their parent are particularly prone to anxiety. Are they eating properly? Have they fallen and become stranded? Are they feeling lonely? Why don't they answer the phone? Fears can be especially intense when the parent has Alzheimer's or another form of dementia. Are they endangering themselves in some way? Have they turned on the gas without lighting it? Have they wandered from their home and become lost? Or, if the parent is depressed and suicidal, the carer wonders if they will carry out their threat to take their own life. If you live some distance from your parent, you may be uptight over being able to reach them quickly in an emergency.

Other carers worry about the care they give. Are they doing enough to ensure their parent stays as fit as possible? Do they understand their parent's needs sufficiently? Worries may extend into the future. Will they be able to carry on caring indefinitely without risking a collapse in their own health? If they do fall ill, who then will take care of their parent?

A hallmark of caring for someone who is disabled is the experience of uncertainty. Many carers say how much easier it would be if only they knew how long the caring would have to go on. You may have taken on a commitment to caring in the belief it would last for only a short time. Five years later, perhaps even 10, you find yourself in the same situation, wondering how much longer you will be able to cope if your parent's health continues to deteriorate.

Anxiety goes hand-in-hand with stress. Though many of your worries are genuine, there is a danger that they will grow out of proportion, cultivated by the state of tension in which you find yourself. Anxiety takes root in minds which are not very peaceful or tranquil. Worry is pointless in a context in which you are powerless to act – and yet it can so easily plague the carer. Some find that it helps to try to live for each day, tackling the challenges of the present, and trying not to dwell on the potential difficulties which lie ahead.

Conflict

One of the worst dimensions of the emotional turmoil faced by many carers is their own conflicting feelings. Affection vies with resentment. Fulfilment is challenged by despair. Commitment is undermined by anxiety. Moods fluctuate. One minute you feel calm and in control; the next you feel you are drowning in a sea of guilt and depression. You may find it difficult to understand how you can, in the same instant, feel deep compassion and intense anger towards your parent. You grumble about their shortcomings, yet you know in your heart of hearts that you will always care for them.

You might also feel conflict in the arena of priorities. You feel pushed and pulled in all directions. Your various friends and relatives are all tugging for your attention. You are caught between the generations, forced to divide your meagre energies between your grandchildren, children, partner and parent. Perhaps there are other claims upon your time which create a dilemma: your work, your voluntary activities, your charity involvement, your leisure pursuits – all clamour for a share of your commitment. Yet you are only human; you cannot be all things to all people. You must set yourself priorities, and this can be a disturbing exercise (as described below).

As a carer, you may feel torn in two by conflict in the areas of feelings and priorities. You cannot live with this pressure: you need to find ways to protect yourself from overload.

Coping

There is no universal prescription for dealing with troublesome feelings. We are each different and will find our own unique ways of working through our anger, guilt and anxiety. There are some strategies which seem to be of general use, however, and which might enable you to find your own survival plan.

Face up to your feelings

There is little you can do to help yourself if you are unwilling to admit to your feelings. You may have an underlying fear that being open with yourself will bring into focus how bad your situation has become. Or you may sense that guilt threatens to overwhelm you if you confess to the depth of anger and resentment which is within you. But only when you can name the animal within can you start to tame it.

For those of us with a British upbringing this is somewhat alien. We learn to bottle up and conceal our feelings. For men, especially, it is a source of pride not to weep or show any sign of falling apart. Unfortunately, suppressed feelings have a way of finding their escape. If you fail now to face up to some of the pain you are hiding, you may find yourself forced to confront it later on. Of course, you are entitled to ignore your feelings in the interests of managing each day's challenges. If you decide it is better to avoid collapse and risk being unable to continue, then that is your prerogative. But be aware that in years to come, you may have to invest time and energy in the process of unearthing those lost feelings and putting them finally to rest. The choice is yours!

Don't expect to be perfect

A common feeling among carers is the expectation of perfection in themselves. If they cannot match up to the all-loving, all-patient, all-caring son or daughter which they aspire to be, they condemn themselves to a life of remorse. As a carer, you must learn early on that it is unrealistic to hope that you will never lose your temper or feel frustrated. Your responses are, to a large extent, natural and understandable. It would require a saint never to feel cross with a person whose dementia causes them to repeat incessantly the same meaningless phrase, or to pace ceaselessly up and down a room. It would be unfair to ask you to feel no regret over the lost opportunities and fading dreams which caring may have brought.

Even people with the best of relationships with their parent have rows and misunderstandings. They almost come as standard in parent-child relationships. Why else do so many carers confess that it would be far easier to care for someone else's parent than their own? Just because a person is sick or weak does not mean that you cannot sometimes feel irritated by them.

Quit the desire to don the super-hero guise each day. Caring may be bringing you face-to-face with a side of your personality you would rather avoid – but this 'weakness' comes from your being a deeply loving person. Never forget that you are doing a great service to your parent, not to mention your country, in committing your time and energy to caring. There is not a carer alive who would not own to the sorts of feelings of which you feel ashamed. Be kind to yourself, and accept the praise which may occasionally come your way. You do deserve it.

Find an outlet

Painful feelings can grow out of all proportion if kept within. You can feel as though you are carrying a heavy weight around. Try and find a place where you can unburden yourself of your pain. Sometimes carers take to writing down how they feel. Putting feelings into words can be deeply releasing. Some even find themselves composing poems which express their feelings. Perhaps you could keep a journal in which you record your reactions to things that happen. Looking back over your entries after a while might enable you to identify a pattern. This process can go a long way towards shedding light on the complexity of your feelings. Understanding the nature of the pain can then help you deal with it.

Another useful outlet can be talking about your feelings to a trusted friend or relative. You may feel reticent over confiding what to you may seem unmentionable feelings. It will be necessary to select carefully a sensitive listener, who you feel sure will not be quick to judge. Not everyone who asks 'How are you?' is genuinely keen to hear your reply. A good listener is one who reflects back to you the feelings you have described. They act as a mirror, showing you more clearly what you feel. The bugbear of so many carers is that people are slow to listen but quick to offer unwanted advice. You lack the energy to implement their suggestions. You merely want a conversation which can act as a safety valve, allowing you to let off steam for a few minutes.

You may be amazed at the benefit which talking about your feelings can have. It can offer a tremendous sense of release, simply to realize that someone understands and cares about how you feel. A friend who rings regularly to find out how you are feeling is a friend indeed!

An outlet which many carers find a great release is laughter. Finding the funny side of tough situations often enables them to persevere. Maintaining your sense of humour may become a crucial weapon in the war against despair.

In 1983, Margaret's dad died, and with his loss came the realization that it fell to her, as the single daughter of her parents, to take responsibility for her mum, Alice. Alice had depended very much upon her husband. The shock of being without him caused her Parkinson's disease to advance rapidly. Sadly, the drug she was then prescribed worsened her condition further, and had an unfortunate effect on her personality.

Margaret had always been closer to her father, and felt that her mother sensed and resented this. Their relationship, then, did not lend itself to constant exposure, so Margaret initially kept her own rented home, which was attached to the hospital where she worked, and looked after her mum at weekends. After a year or two, however, it became clear that Alice was no longer coping and Margaret returned to live at home, while continuing her demanding job, to which she travelled 11 miles each day. An increased group of people were needed to help Alice during the day, and Margaret's 'leisure time' was completely dominated by caring. Sometimes her mum would say hurtful things; at other times her Parkinson's caused her to be rigid and difficult for Margaret to lift. The idea of any kind of social life was a dream.

Margaret's brother and sister-in-law gave support only when Margaret was away, and did not, therefore, recognize the demands she faced. To some extent, Margaret was her own worst enemy. Presenting a capable front, it was easy for those around her to assume she was coping, when actually she struggled bitterly with her daily marathon. Then came a surprise which was to prove a lifeline for Margaret. Quite by chance, she met up with a friend from her nursing training. Elaine was quick to understand and respond to Alice and to Margaret's needs. She gave considerable practical support, helping bath Alice and changing her bed. Most significantly, though, she listened to Margaret and cared about her. Margaret then realized how isolated she had become. It was wonderful to have a friend, closer than she had known in her entire life. And other friends also stepped in to ease the pressure on Margaret and to befriend Alice. They gave invaluable help and companionship.

At about that time, Margaret also changed jobs. She found her new job, in a hospice, fitted more easily with the demands of home life and gave her the space to reflect on what caring meant for her. Looking back, she can see that in many ways her prayers for strength were answered. That she remained fit and well was a marvel in itself. That she discovered a friend who was kinder than a sister remains a source of deep pleasure and gratitude. But more than that, Margaret feels that caring has made her a warmer person.

As the years passed, though, it became increasingly difficult for Margaret to manage, until eventually moving Alice any distance was virtually impossible. By this stage, after nearly 10 years of caring and working full-time, Margaret was exhausted. Eight weeks of respite care did little to restore her strength. She had to accept that Alice would be more appropriately cared for in a nursing home. On Alice's eightieth birthday, therefore, she entered the home where she was to spend the final 15 months of her life. Margaret never came to terms with having to hand over caring. She found visits traumatic, and coped only with Elaine's presence and support.

Alice's death shattered Margaret, for she had never had space to grieve for the earlier loss of her father. She felt intensely the pain of being left 'alone'. In the year since Alice's death, Margaret feels she owes a great deal to Elaine, who has helped her cope. She is in the process of moving house, and hopes to take early retirement before too long. Only then does she expect to recover fully from the extreme physical, mental and emotional strain she has faced for so many years. Remembering the gruelling stress she endured, she wonders now how she ever survived.

Consider therapy

You may have problems over confiding in a friend or relative. Perhaps you would feel more comfortable talking to a stranger – or perhaps you feel that your emotional difficulties require professional help. If so, you may find counselling to be of assistance. As we noted in Chapter 4, counselling is available on the National Health Service through GP referral, but there are also voluntary and charitable organizations which offer counselling (ask at your Citizens' Advice Bureau).

A counsellor should be able to help you unravel your feelings and to understand where they come from. The counsellor will work with you towards resolving the conflicts and coping better with emotional challenges. Many carers find counselling to be of great value: they discover the need to resolve difficulties which stem from many years back, and which caring has brought to the fore.

Counselling does not always go far enough in helping a person resolve emotional difficulties. In addition, your GP may be able to prescribe antidepressant medication. Alternatively, your GP may prefer to refer you for psychiatric help, rather than prescribing anti-depressant drugs himself. The psychiatrist may deem that you require, as well as or instead of antidepressants, some form of cognitive therapy. Perhaps a psychiatric nurse will work with you towards challenging the negative thought-processes which have become ingrained, and so led you to a state of continual anxiety. Or perhaps a psychiatrist will refer you to a group for relaxation classes. Relaxation skills can be an invaluable tool for carers.

GPs vary in their awareness of carers' needs. Some assume that their responsibility lies only towards the elderly person who is sick. Others have a broader understanding of the strains carers face, and recognize that they have a role in supporting them. Don't be afraid to ask for help for yourself, and persist if you meet with insensitivity at first.

Join a carers group

Caring is one of those experiences in life which you can never fully comprehend unless you have been through it. Carers can find that other people betray a hopeless lack of awareness in the things they say. Talking with other carers, on the other hand, can be entirely different. They seem to know instinctively what you are going through. They don't hold it against you if you admit to feeling furious towards your parent; they scarcely bat an eyelid when you say even that you occasionally have the urge to strangle the person! Carers have been there before, and the very fact that they share your feelings is a comfort in itself.

That is why a network of carers groups has been formed the length and breadth of the country. Sometimes the groups are geared specifically for carers of someone with a particular condition – the Alzheimer's Disease Society, for instance, has many support groups. Sometimes groups are set up for people from a particular ethnic background – for example, you might find a group for Asian carers. Perhaps the largest proportion of groups, however, are for all carers, regardless of their relative's age or disability. Even carers in vastly differing situations share many of the same feelings.

Groups vary in the frequency, timing and location of meetings. However, they all aim to create a network of carers who can build friendship and trust with one another. Groups provide a safe place in which to off-load anxieties and grievances. Many carers find they discover useful tips and information from other members. Occasionally also groups are active in campaigning for better services for carers. Some groups have social events, others have a regular programme of speakers. You do not have to leave a group when your relative goes into a home or dies. This may be the time when you are most in need of the support of other carers.

There are a number of ways to find out about groups in your area. An obvious place to turn would be to the head office of the Carers National Association, to which many carers support groups are affiliated. Alternatively, your social services department should have details of groups. You may also find a list with your local council for voluntary service or Citizens' Advice Bureau. Sometimes groups are advertised in public places such as GPs' surgeries and libraries.

You may feel that you do not wish to spend your scarce free time talking and thinking about caring. Perhaps you would rather use respite care to do something completely unrelated, which takes your mind off caring. Each of us is different. Carers groups do not suit everyone. Even if you are loath to attend meetings, however, you could still be part of a carers network. It is an advantage to join the Carers National Association. The fee for membership is modest, and the benefits great. You would receive their regular bi-monthly magazine, called *The Carer*, with information on such things as changes in the law and useful equipment. You will feel that you belong to a vast work-force and have an organization which can act as your mouthpiece. Belonging to the Carers National Association is as near as you are likely to get to belonging to a trade union which can protect your rights. Many local carers support groups also have a regular newsletter which can keep you abreast of issues of importance to carers in your area.

Above all, belonging to a carers group gives you the feeling that you are not alone. It can shake you out of the belief that no one before you has been through what you are facing. It can give you the courage to believe there is light at the end of the tunnel.

Conclusion

It cannot be doubted that caring provokes a torrent of feelings, many unwelcome. If you are able to confront honestly the pain you face, and work through its implications, you will find that you grow as an individual and in your knowledge of yourself. Through all the turmoil can come a depth of maturity, empathy and compassion which is a fitting reward.

6

Discovering survival strategies

When you first took on a commitment to caring for your parent, you may have believed yourself to be accepting obligations which would last only a little while. Perhaps you hoped your parent would regain their independence. Or maybe you feared they would not live much longer. But unless your parent has an acute, terminal illness, it is unlikely that your experience of caring will be short-lived.

Assuming the situation to be temporary, you may well have put your own life on hold, as it were, and absorbed yourself in the task of helping your parent. In the longer term, this is not a viable response. Exhaustion and collapse beckon – unless you take steps to make your life-style manageable for the indefinite future. In particular, you may need actively to seek strategies to help you cope with the demands of caring. These mechanisms for coping will vary from person to person. One person's tonic may well lack appeal for another. You need to give serious and careful thought to devising plans which can make a potentially unendurable situation endurable. Here are some keys to coping which other carers have found to be important.

Remember to look after yourself

It may seem an obvious statement, but carers' needs are as important as the needs of the person being cared for. Sometimes, however, it can appear to carers that they don't really matter. The person at the centre of medical attention, for one thing, is their parent. They can feel like a mere appendage within the therapeutic environment. Solicitous questions are asked of their parent by friends and relatives. Even some of the guides written to help carers focus almost exclusively on being an effective carer, and offering the best possible support.

You may feel hurt that no one around you asks after you. Not a single person seems concerned for your welfare. You too may become convinced of the fact that your needs take second place to those of your parent. You need to take stock and adjust your thinking very quickly. It may seem hard, but if nobody else seems likely to take your needs into consideration, you yourself will have to take steps to make sure they are not neglected. Try not to wallow in self-pity and pursue the martyr's path simply to make a point. This approach could lead you into difficulty. Your resources are only finite. If stretched beyond the limit, you might well snap. Your own mental and physical health could collapse. Or you may find yourself losing control and hitting out at your parent in anger, in a way you will later regret. Frail elderly people are vulnerable. It has been known for them to suffer physical, emotional, mental and even sexual abuse at the hands of relatives. Would you want to speak cruel words which echoed in your conscience long after they had been uttered? Don't be driven to breaking point. Be sensible: find ways of making life tolerable for yourself before it becomes too late.

The risk to your parent of pushing yourself too hard is an important factor – but far more significant is the truth that you are important as an individual in your own right. Sometimes your parent's preference will not always be best for you. While give and take need to come into play, and compromises are reached on occasions, it is sometimes necessary to stand up for what you want. In any conflict between you and your parent, there is no law that says your parent's will must prevail. You are no longer a child who must obey their promptings. Their disability may exert a powerful pressure – but it provides no justification for demolishing your identity.

It may help to think in terms of the role of paid carers. Particularly if working in the state sector, paid carers benefit from laws and structures which govern their working conditions and protect them from abuse and exploitation. They may have recourse to a trade union if they feel their rights have been infringed. They have an expectation of reasonable hours of work in conditions of safety and comfort. You have no such protection, and it requires determination on your part to ensure that you are not taken for granted and used to another person's advantage.

All this may seem elementary, an unnecessary labouring of the point. Many carers, however, have genuine difficulty in accepting that it is OK to ask for help and accept breaks. They would much rather drive themselves beyond the point of common sense than go against their parent's desires and enlist help, for example. So pronounced has been this tendency among carers, that carers groups have been known to offer assertiveness training. Carers have been given guidance over how to persist in asking for services, and how to resist the objections of relatives.

Any doctor or social worker worthy of their role will see your needs as of critical importance. If they fail to understand, you will have to insist on convincing them. Too many carers become experts at presenting a capable exterior. Everyone around them marvels at their ability to cope, when underneath they are fighting to survive. It is true that it may involve a dent to your pride to admit that you are not invincible, that life is hard, that you would grasp help with both hands if it were offered. In your search for coping mechanisms, it is vital to accept that your needs should not be sacrificed at the altar of another person's disability.

Jackie finds it difficult to remember a time when she didn't look after her mum, Lydia. Even as a little child, she would rush to Lydia's aid during her epileptic fits. She and her older brother, Mark, would try to break their mum's fall and then wait while she came round.

One day, when Jackie was just 10 and Mark 12, Lydia had a fit when she was alone at home and her foot fell into the fire. It was so badly burned that the leg had to be amputated below the knee. Lydia learned to walk short distances with an artificial leg, but when she went out she used a wheelchair. Mark and Jackie would take it in turns to push Lydia's wheelchair. As they lived in a village, they caught a bus into town. One of the children would help Lydia with the steps, while the other put the wheelchair on the bus. Some days Jackie would have to stay away from school to take her mum to the hospital. Their father, Ian, had left work to look after Lydia, so when Jackie left school at 16 she went out to work for a few years. She and Mark would help out at weekends. Very gradually it became Jackie's role to give support at home.

A few years later Lydia had a stroke. Jackie found she was taking a lot of time off work, so decided to give up her job in order to help her dad. It was not long before she found that she was fulfilling the main caring role, as her dad was becoming older and less fit. After a short time, he had a heart attack. Although Ian recovered, he felt insecure if left alone, so the pressure was on Jackie to be at home with her parents. After a second heart attack, Ian became badly depressed. He was admitted to hospital. As the months passed it dawned on Jackie that he would not be coming home. She would now have to care for her mum alone. Lydia and Jackie visited Ian regularly during those final 14 months of his life. When he died in 1994, he was 77.

Caring has been a way of life for Jackie for so long, yet it is only in the last couple of years that she has been able to describe herself as a carer. She recognizes that her life has been restricted. She remembers, when she was a teenager, that her dad tried to dissuade her from dating: he warned Jackie that, should she leave home to marry, Lydia would have to go into a home because he would not manage her on his own. It became difficult for Jackie to have relationships. Lydia too is reluctant to allow Jackie much freedom. She likes to make sure that

Jackie is never too far away and can get home quickly if needed.

Only recently has Jackie learned how important it is for her to have her own life. She is most appreciative of the breaks she has when a Crossroads care attendant visits for a few hours each week, and when her mum is at the day centre she attends twice weekly. Jackie is aware of how limited her life is, and there have been times when she has felt angry and frustrated. The best way to cope, she feels, is to focus on the good things about her life. She genuinely considers it a privilege to care for her mum. She loves her company and enjoys the outings they have several times each week.

Jackie is now 30. She lives for each day instead of trying to see into an unpredictable future. Facing what lies ahead has become easier since she has discovered that she is a person in her own right, and not just her parent's daughter. She realizes that, though it was difficult to let go and allow another person to look after her mum, accepting breaks from caring has given her the scope to be herself. Despite the hardship of her life, Jackie feels a deep love for her mum which compels her to offer constant care and companionship.

Hang on to outside interests

Keeping hold of pursuits outside the home, and activities within, can undeniably be a battle for carers. You can be made to feel guilty if you go out. Friends are resented. Time away from home is begrudged. Or, if you try to get on with an activity which provides a diversion from caring at home, you may face constant interruptions as your parent finds reasons to call for your help. You wonder sometimes if it is worth the struggle to persevere.

These activities are *not* a luxury, something without which you can easily manage. It is no exaggeration to say that they represent your very identity. They are the things which make you your own person. They offer also the relief of a momentary escape from the stress of caring. They can help to lift you out of an introspective preoccupation with the problems and challenges, giving you renewed vigour in facing them again. What is more, the outside activities – be they paid work, voluntary work or simply hobbies – are an investment for the future. Without them, you risk finding your life empty, devoid of activity and structure, when you lose your parent. There may be a price to pay for engaging your energies outside the home or caring situation. Life may feel like a continual balancing act. But the price will be well worth paying in terms of your sense of identity.

You must choose for yourself the type of activity to which you turn for identity. For some it is merely a continuation of a previous occupation, though perhaps with reduced hours. For others, it is the discovery of a new hobby or interest. Some carers find it therapeutic to spend time each day in their garden. Others lose themselves in books about topics which absorb them. Creative tasks, such as cookery and embroidery, can take on a new enjoyment. You need to discover an activity, if you don't have one already, which you will first and foremost enjoy, an activity which will stimulate your mind and cause you to exercise your creativity. This outside interest has proved the secret of survival for many carers. A simple channel for self-expression can make a huge difference.

Keep hold of relationships that matter

Another key to retaining your equilibrium through the turbulent years of caring may be to insist on keeping in touch with people who are dear to you. We have seen in previous chapters how easily relationships can be pushed aside by the demands of caring. You no longer have the freedom to meet up with friends and relatives whenever you choose. Travelling to see them may become difficult. You may lack the energy to write letters and make phone calls. Perhaps most significant is the subtle pressure exerted by your parent increasingly to confine your circle of friends and relations. Someone who is themself housebound and isolated may well resent the contacts and social outlets of their carer.

Another factor in keeping in touch is the willingness of your friends and relatives to accommodate your new life-style. Maintaining a friendship may involve them in having to travel to you more often, and cope with your parent's disability. Particularly where a parent has a condition like Alzheimer's disease, carers can feel hurt and confused by the reactions of friends. They understand the fear and anxiety of friends over being in the company of someone with dementia – but they feel let down by people who stay away. There may also be that within the carer which keeps people at arm's length through embarrassment. They may be acutely aware, for example, of smells generated through incontinence.

It is common for carers to claim that the experience of caring reveals their friends in their true light. Sometimes they are surprised over people who turn out to be mere fair weather friends, while others, who had seemed less close, continue to visit and show great kindness. Relationships do involve commitment. You may be tempted to give up on friendships outside your home. There is a danger, however, of becoming too heavily dependent on your parent. You risk severe loneliness when they die. Better to insist on seeing your children, grandchildren and friends on a regular basis. In this way you will be more likely to receive the love and nurture you need for your demanding role. And when you lose your parent, you will have a circle of people to support you and help you find a new life.

Loneliness steals up slowly on some carers. By the time they realize how isolated they have become, it is too late to re-establish old friendships. It takes courage, but it is a wise strategy then to take steps to discover a new network of relationships. Some take up new hobbies and studies, others join carers groups, others belong to pen-pal clubs. It is no simple task to recreate your social network from a position of almost complete confinement in the home. But, like maintaining other interests, it will be an investment for the future.

Jack has been involved in caring for both his parents. Arthur, Jack's father, suffered from arthritis and was housebound for the last 12 years of his life, dying at the age of 90 in 1987. Between them, Jack and his mother, Betty, managed to keep him at home for all but the final three months of his life. This necessitated a move of house to a property with downstairs facilities. The long years spent caring for her husband took their toll on Betty's health, so that she now has arthritis, pernicious anaemia and short-term memory loss, and is deaf and partially sighted. Being housebound and deaf has caused her to lose confidence in company and to rely heavily on Jack.

Jack retired from working as a chartered mechanical engineer in 1994. Until that time, he had fitted caring for his mum around a full-time job. The help he receives extends only to twice-weekly Meals on Wheels and a visit from a bath-nurse once a week. All other aspects of caring fall to Jack. Jack consequently feels his life is very restricted. He has not taken a holiday for five years, and confines himself to occasional days out. He feels he is always 'on call'.

Despite these limitations, however, Jack dislikes the idea of losing his mum, who is now 92. He is determined to keep her living at home with him for as long as possible, because he knows how unpleasant she found the visits they paid to his father when he was in a residential home. He feels it would destroy Betty if she were ever to move to a home. At the age of 61, Jack has no close family living nearby. His only sister emigrated to New Zealand over 30 years ago. Betty has been a close companion over the years, and currently a future without her holds only loneliness, Jack feels. To help broaden his social contacts, he attends evening classes. He also goes to meetings of his local carers association. While caring has proved a limiting experience for Jack, he is apprehensive about its alternative.

Insist on breaks

Respite care is rarely an optional extra, something without which carers can easily survive. It is as vital for carers' well-being as having weekends off is for a paid worker. This is not to say, however, that establishing regular time away from caring is easily achieved. As we have noted already, in previous chapters, numerous obstacles must often be first overcome. There may be opposition from your parent, who quite naturally does not relish the prospect of being looked after by a stranger who lacks your instinctive grasp of their needs. Emotional blackmail can be cleverly used to persuade you that to take a break would be an act of cruelty towards a person who depends for their very existence, they imply, on your perpetual presence.

Quite apart from your parent's ploys to avoid respite care, there may be a war being waged within your own mind. While recognizing your need for rest, you may also be racked with guilt over the potential consequences for your parent of entrusting them to outside care. Even in situations where both parent and carer have accepted that respite care is necessary, finding appropriate alternatives may prove troublesome. Invariably, services provided for carers are in great demand. Finding a respite bed in a hospital or residential home may seem impossible. There may be a long waiting-list for a service like Crossroads. You may face an uphill struggle in proving that you need support, and in gaining an entitlement to a service. You may feel bad about accepting support which would then not be available to a carer in more extreme need. Patience and perseverance will almost certainly be required.

Too many carers are sweet-natured, obliging and self-deprecating. It is with great reluctance that they enter into heated arguments to establish their entitlements. You may need to learn to be more forceful in asserting your rights. After all, your requests are modest: the labour you invest in caring is making a huge saving for the welfare state, which might otherwise have to fund a place in a nursing or residential home.

To the outsider, it makes perfect sense to claim that breaks are vital for anyone in a demanding caring role. Sadly, the issue can seem less clear to carers. It is in the interests of your parent and yourself that you respect the needs of your body, allowing it sufficient rest and relaxation. Only by accepting regular respite will you be able to continue caring for any length of time.

Guard moments of relaxation

Life may have become so fraught that you have forgotten what it is like to sit quietly cogitating with a cup of tea. Stress may have become a constant companion. Several things can contribute to the stress faced by carers. An obvious source is the sheer volume of tasks crying out for attention. Some carers are effectively running two households – cooking, cleaning and washing for their parent as well as in their own home. Many have paid work to fit around the demands of caring. Carers often express their frustration over the lack of time available by wishing that there were more hours in a day. It is not only the thousand and one things to do that generate stress, however. Caring often occurs in a highly charged atmosphere. Emotions can run high. Anger, frustration, guilt, grief and anxiety can contribute to an emotional overload which leads to intolerable stress levels.

The symptoms of stress vary from carer to carer. Some experience unpleasant physical side-effects, such as palpitations, high blood-pressure and insomnia. Others gradually find themselves losing control of their feelings: they have surges of panic and fear, they burst into tears at the slightest provocation, or they find themselves losing their temper uncharacteristically.

Stress is to be minimized if at all possible. The secret of doing this is to cultivate relaxation skills. In extreme cases, a GP will refer a carer for relaxation classes, perhaps run in a local hospital or clinic. You may be surprised by the kinds of people who are helped by such classes. People from all walks of life struggle to stay calm and need guidance over controlling their feelings. In most cases, however, books and tapes, available in libraries and book shops, provide adequate information on relaxation. Their aim is to teach you how to relax, whatever your situation. For instance, the guidance may help you to be aware of tension building up in your muscles, or it may encourage you to picture in your mind's eye scenes which have a calming effect.

In time, you may discover your own formula for reducing stress. Instead of concentrating on the awfulness of a situation, you may learn to say to yourself, 'However bad this situation is, I have coped before, and I will manage again'. Carers can learn to focus on positives, and not waste their energy thinking about the bad aspects of life. Sometimes, if you force yourself to smile, you may even catch yourself feeling happier after a little while!

Think about the ways in which you have unwound in the past. Having a soothing bath, reading a novel, or taking the dog for a walk are all common ways of relaxing. You might even be able to persuade someone to buy you a massage session as a Christmas present! Be aware of your levels of stress, and do all you can to keep them under control.

Don't be afraid to ask for help

Above all, the key to coping with caring is being willing to ask for help. Going it alone is rarely a wise strategy. Many carers fall into the trap of resenting the people who fail to offer help, without realizing that they are sending out signals indicating that they can cope very well on their own. Friends and relatives cannot be expected to understand instinctively how much support you need. There is no guarantee that they will agree to it, even if you do explain what is required – but at least you will have given them the opportunity. However deep your pride in doing everything single-handed to support your parent, there will be no medals for running yourself into the ground.

Martha has experienced two types of caring. For the first seven years after her mother, Eve's, stroke she continued to work full-time as a social worker in a psychiatric hospital. Home-helps came in daily to care for Eve while Martha was at work. Over the years, however, Martha's resources shrank, until she eventually suffered complete burn-out as a result of the accumulated stress and exhaustion.

While recovering, she spent time thinking about the future. She decided that Eve's life had been very difficult. She had lived with many people imposing their ways on her while Martha was at work, and many hours of solitude. As a result, her speech had become scarcely coherent. Martha decided to take early retirement and devote more time to caring for Eve. Their relationship became much closer, and Eve was visibly calmer and happier.

Martha feels she was at an advantage in having spent her working life in the world of caring. Firstly, her counselling background had taught her that painful feelings need to be confronted, and long-standing difficulties in relationships resolved. She feels that carers need help, perhaps from a counsellor, in coming to terms with the effects of past events upon their present relationship with their parent. Otherwise, the carer can become deeply unhappy and resentful. For herself, Martha was able to realize that the experience of hospitalization twice over, and evacuation during the war, had left lingering hurt since childhood. She grew also to understand the pain her mum had felt over those experiences. She was grateful for the opportunity to work through the consequences of events which had left a deep impression on her.

A second benefit of her professional background was that it enabled her to keep in touch with the outside world while based largely at home. Former colleagues would refer people to her for counselling. She also set up a support group for professional people facing stress at work. She invited them regularly to her home for a meal, so that they could talk together about the problems they faced. The group still meets to this day. Members grew to love and value Eve as much as she enjoyed their visits.

Eve and Martha developed an understanding over the need for Martha to have breaks. They would use their attendance allowance to pay for respite carers. Eve was pleased when Martha returned from the badminton court refreshed and full of news.

In total, Martha spent 16 years caring for Eve. She feels she learned a great deal about herself and about life. She has three pieces of advice for other carers:

- She encourages them to spend time tackling and resolving long-standing difficulties in their relationship with their parent.
- She feels it is wise to use attendance allowance to buy respite care, so that the carer can have regular breaks to pursue their own interests.
- She suggests finding ways of maintaining links with a life outside the home so that, once caring is finished, it is not so hard to pick up the pieces and find areas of continuity.

Conclusion

Carers who fail to care for themselves do so at their peril. However noble and saintly their approach, it is humanly impossible to survive this degree of neglect in the long term. Recognizing your own needs, enlisting support, and cultivating those interests and relationships which keep you in touch with who you are, will pay dividends. You will reap the benefits in the present, with heightened self-esteem and self-possession making you a better and more fulfilled carer. But you will also reap long-term benefits. Yes, there can be life after caring – if you are sure to guard your identity and health, despite the pressures of looking after a disabled person.

7
Reviewing the situation

When you commit yourself to offering support to a disabled parent, you are not entering into an irreversible arrangement. In the early days, fired by a desire to be of whatever help you can, you possibly won't anticipate reaching a stage where you can no longer cope single-handed. In your optimism, however, you may have failed to take into account the fact that your parent may remain dependent on you for a very long time, and may become increasingly frail. How will your reserves of strength and patience be holding up ten years down the line?

Carers frequently live with the pressures of hastily-made promises. Their parent has begged never to be placed in a care-home. In an effort to comfort and reassure, the carer (or even perhaps another relative) has offered rash guarantees that this will be avoided at all costs. Some carers need not even ask their parent's views on full-time care – they know instinctively how they would react. Perhaps they have witnessed their parent's response to another older person being admitted to a home.

Dorothy's experience of caring goes back 15 years. She still lives in the house to which she and her parents, George and Violet, moved in Coronation year. When George and Violet were in their 70s, a paternal aunt of Dorothy's came to live with them at the age of 90. She lived in a self-contained flat within the house, and it was Dorothy who gave her most support – though at that time enjoying a successful teaching career. Dorothy was at her aunt's side when she died. Afterwards, Dorothy moved into her aunt's rooms, much to the annoyance of her mum, Violet, who had little understanding of Dorothy's desire for independence.

Dorothy says that, had she known in advance what caring for her mum would be like, she doubts she could have done it. For a long time, Dorothy and George failed to identify in Violet the symptoms of Alzheimer's disease. Although she read about and studied the disease, nothing could have prepared Dorothy for the reality of Alzheimer's. The condition emerged at a time when Dorothy herself was ill with heart problems and a tumour, which, though successfully removed, left kidney damage. And so it came about that, at the very moment when Dorothy took early retirement from a fulfilling and exciting job as deputy head of a middle school, Violet's need for care became evident.

For Dorothy, caring presented an opportunity to work through many of the painful feelings connected with her relationship with her mum. Through her entire life, Dorothy had sensed that her mum had never accepted her as she was. She felt her mum would much rather she had followed the path of her younger sister, who had married and had children. Her response to the hurt of feeling misunderstood was to throw herself into caring for her mum. It was truly a renewing experience, to be able to find ways of protecting and comforting her mum through the intense fear which became the hallmark of her Alzheimer's. Dorothy's only sadness is that it was too late to connect with Violet, to experience the kind of mother-daughter relationship she so craved.

Nevertheless, the opportunity to give her mum comfort, to help nurse the acute eczema she developed, and simply provide a constant, caring presence, helped soothe Dorothy's disappointment. She feels that, had she been deprived of the caring that so dominated her life, she would have sunk into desperation.

Dorothy had her dad for support, though he had never been able to express his feelings. In his 80s, and nearly blind, he was unable to give his wife physical care, but he shared with Dorothy the pain of witnessing Violet's steady decline and remorseless loss of every semblance of her previous self. While emotionally reserved, George had always been the parent with whom Dorothy had been able to talk freely.

Sometimes the sheer strain of caring for a mother with Alzheimer's left Dorothy with an agony of conflicting feelings: there were moments when she hoped her ordeal would soon end, simply because she lacked the energy to go on – yet she dreaded losing her mum, and wanted to preserve her life for as long as possible. Despite the almost unbearable pressure, however, Dorothy found the process of taking short breaks from caring almost too difficult to be worthwhile. Her mum battled against going to a day-centre two days a week. As her condition worsened, George and Dorothy needed her to have two weeks' respite care in a nursing home in every six weeks. Dorothy found it so painful to face her mum's distress on being left, that a cousin took Violet to the home. To add insult to injury, and because of a change in the law, after the second break Dorothy and George were faced with a huge bill for the total cost of the respite care.

On many occasions, Violet had pleaded with George never to let her go into a nursing home, and he had promised to keep her at home.

As her condition deteriorated, and she became doubly incontinent and unable to move, the promise hung heavily over Dorothy and George. With sad hearts, they planned to move Violet to a unit where she would receive the care she needed, knowing that the parting from her husband and daughter would destroy her. On the day before the move was due, Violet's condition worsened and she was transferred to hospital, where she died with George and Dorothy by her side. She was 89 and had been married to George for 62 years. The dreaded separation had not been necessary after all – to the continuing relief of George and Dorothy.

Dorothy's focus now, two years after her mum's death, is to cherish each day she has with her dad. Now completely blind, he retains his mental agility and is still able to walk. But the effects of his 90 years are obvious. He freely admits he would not have lived as long had it not been for Dorothy's constant care. He may not wear his heart on his sleeve, but he makes it clear to Dorothy that he values her loving support. Dorothy still lives with the pain of never having heard her mum say that she was the daughter she wanted her to be. But she is glad she was able to offer her mum the love she needed in her dying years. She dreads the future, fearing that her dad will die soon.

With the best will in the world, you cannot as a carer prevent a parent's health declining. As the situation changes, it is important for you to adjust your arrangements for caring.

Accept a changing situation

The context in which you care will vary considerably. No two days may be the same; even within the same day, there may be periods of calm control juxtaposed with frantic moments. A key factor governing fluctuations will be your parent's health. There will be good days, when your parent seems relatively capable – and bad days, when they need more intensive nursing. Infections will affect their health, perhaps to a considerable degree. Then there will be the stages through which their illness or disability passes which, cumulatively, bring steady decline. Demands which you may have found manageable at first, suddenly feel like an intolerable strain.

As your parent's level of dependency rises it may become gradually apparent that their surroundings are no longer suitable. Perhaps there are steps they cannot manage, or pieces of furniture which are uncomfortable or impossible for them to use. It may seem that a move of home is required, perhaps to a sheltered flat with a warden on call, or even to your own home. There may be other options, besides a move of home. If your parent was assessed for support a while ago, it may be that the package of services now no longer suffices. It will be necessary to contact the care-manager named in the original agreement, to see if it is possible to add extra support to the care currently provided. Perhaps the moment has come when your parent could benefit from Meals on Wheels, or from regular attendance at a day-centre.

Your care-manager does not expect your situation to remain the same. They know that they will need to review your parent's situation, offering a steadily increasing level of support. They will also be concerned for your health and well-being, if they are doing their job properly. Part of their role is to ensure that you are not overwhelmed by the demands placed upon you by your parent. If signs of stress are emerging, they will see this as a reason for intervening and offering greater support. It can sometimes seem that caring is so draining that it scarcely leaves time to draw breath, let alone conduct regular reviews of the situation. The tendency, then, is for carers to struggle on, continuing to absorb ever-growing demands on their time – perhaps beyond a point at which their own resources suffice. A bout of exhaustion or continual ill-health may then force them to take stock, and realize that the ability to cope and keep on top has deserted them.

In an ideal world, you would be able to discuss with your parent how each of you is managing and assess the need for more outside help. If your parent is sympathetic to your needs, it helps a great deal in searching for an appropriate and sensitive package of support. But if your parent refuses to accept your point of view, and will not acknowledge the strain you are under, you may need to talk through the situation with a friend or professional person who can help you see clearly what is required. Burying your head in the sand will help no one in the long term. Many carers have discovered to their cost that they are not superhuman after all. Monumental efforts to push themselves unduly have resulted in catastrophic collapse.

Accepting increasing levels of support is not conceding defeat; it is merely approaching a declining situation with sense and realism. You need to avoid the temptation to be sucked completely into caring. Your life will continue beyond your parent's death; how much of it will be left if you surrender each minute of every day to caring?

Part of deciding not to bury your head in the sand is being willing to consider the options available for caring for your parent. Finding out about local sheltered housing schemes, and nursing and residential homes, is not an act of betrayal. It is an aspect of long-term planning.

There may come a time when your parent needs to move from their own home to a sheltered housing complex, or from your home to a nursing home. It is helpful to be prepared in advance of that moment. It is useful to have contact with local people who have inside information about such places. Perhaps you know people with friends or relatives in one of the local homes, and you can establish their views on it.

If you can broach the subject of alternative care with your parent at this early stage, you may save heartache later on. You may discover that they have a preference over which home they would choose to live in. Perhaps they have friends or acquaintances in the home, or have heard good reports. If you were able to visit the home with your parent, it may help them at some later stage when a move becomes unavoidable. You would be less likely then to make a decision based more on haste than good judgement. It may also be easier to involve your parent at this stage than later on, in the aftermath perhaps of an accident or acute illness. It may be that the nursing or residential home favoured by you or your parent offers respite care. This provides an excellent opportunity for your parent to experience the home, and get to know staff and residents. You may find that they gradually warm to the idea of living there, so that when a move eventually becomes advisable, the process is less traumatic.

A time to hand over

The decision to relinquish full-time care of a parent can be extremely distressing. For those with a sensitive conscience, it can feel as though a loved one is being abandoned, dumped in the care of someone else. It can represent a failure to honour a promise to care, come what may.

Seeking residential or nursing care, however, may become the only option available, for a variety of reasons. It may simply become impossible for you to care for your parent at home: it may have become too difficult for you to lift them; it may be that they require a degree of medical care which cannot be administered at home. Or perhaps a sudden crisis has occurred, such as a stroke, a heart attack or a bad fall, meaning that your parent has been admitted to hospital. Staff gently discourage you from considering taking your parent back home and recommend a nursing home.

It may be that the decision to find residential or nursing care has resulted less from your parent's growing needs, than from your own failing strength. The effect of caring over many years can be devastating. You may have reached a point of complete physical and emotional collapse. Or you may simply have lost the impetus to care, and find you are becoming impatient and frustrated. Then there may be other parties to consider. You may fear the effect that caring is having on your children, for instance, and wish to shield them from the care of someone so sick. Or you may fear the breakdown of your marriage.

Dealing with practicalities

Perhaps uppermost in your mind are the many arrangements that are necessary – only when the practical details have been sorted out, may you be able to tackle some of your feelings about it.

You need to contact your social services department before your parent can be allocated a place in a home. If your parent is still at home, you must contact your care-manager, if you already have one. If not, then contact your social services or social work department. If your parent is in hospital, there should be a member of staff available to ensure arrangements are made prior to discharge. You need to ask them to contact social services for you.

Your parent will be assessed and, according to their level of need, offered a place in a residential or nursing home. It may be necessary for you to put across that you have reached the end of your ability to cope, so that the care manager can see that it would be unreasonable to expect you to continue. The social services department should be able to give you a list of homes in the area. It will be helpful, however, to pay a visit to those homes you favour, to confirm whether or not they are places in which you expect your parent to thrive. Take your parent with you, if at all possible. After all, this is to be their future home, not yours.

Everyone looks for different features in a home. For some people, privacy is vital: they want to make sure their parent will have a private room. For others, the range of choice available (over such things as when to eat or get up in the morning, or how often to take a bath) is important. Perhaps of critical significance is the atmosphere between residents and staff: do staff treat residents kindly, patiently and respectfully? It is easy to be impressed by attractive décor, but far more telling is the commitment and dedication shown by staff.

It can be quite difficult to find out about a home's record. Many people do not realize that homes are inspected on a regular basis, and that the telephone number of the inspection unit has to be displayed in the home. There is nothing to stop you contacting an inspector for information, particularly if you have concerns about a home. Once you have secured a place in a home, ideally on a trial basis at first, you may need to make arrangements for selling your parent's house, if no one lives in it. Assets your parent owns are used to pay the fees of the home until their value falls to a certain level (set at £16,000 by the 1995 budget). Social services departments can make a legal charge on the property if the disabled person refuses to sell it.

Handling feelings

Ruth's mum, Edna, has never known good health in adult life, and has had numerous periods in hospital. Following the birth of her four children, she had gynaecological operations. She also had two severe bouts of rheumatic fever, has had an operation to remove her gall bladder, has a heart condition and is an insulin-dependent diabetic. Through the years, she has been dogged by numerous other complaints, but has remained remarkably uncomplaining, and indeed, always ready to help others in need.

After Ruth married, her father's eyesight deteriorated gradually, so that he eventually became registered blind and dependent on Edna for support. When he took early retirement, Charles and Edna decided to move from Scotland back to their native Northern Ireland, at about the time the troubles began there. When her mum was ill and in hospital, Ruth travelled over to Belfast with her three children, to be with her dad. Eventually it became apparent that the best solution would be for Edna and Charles to move back to Scotland.

By the time of their return, Charles had developed lung cancer. Edna, too, was in and out of hospital. After Charles's death, Edna stayed with Ruth for several weeks. When she was well enough, she moved into a bungalow some distance from Ruth's home. At first, a daily telephone call enabled Ruth to make sure her mum was managing. As Edna's health deteriorated, though, Ruth began to go over to her mum's bungalow overnight each week to help with housework and cooking. She found a woman to go in several evenings a week, to prepare her mum's evening meal. As time went on, there were occasions when the police or neighbours had to break a window to enter Edna's home and help her. It was clear that she was not coping on her own.

Following periods spent by Edna in various nursing homes, and a six-week stay in hospital, it was suggested that Ruth find a full-time place for Edna. She was strongly advised against caring for her mum in her own home because of Edna's many needs. But Ruth felt she must at least try to care for her mum herself. They had been so close as mother and daughter, never arguing or disagreeing. She loved and admired her mum.

For two years, Ruth struggled with her mum at home, receiving little help from her husband or other friends and relatives. Eventually, physically and emotionally drained, she requested a permanent place in the home where her mum received respite care. When a place became available and Edna moved permanently into the home, however, Ruth felt sad. She felt she had failed her mum. In her heart of hearts, she felt her mum would never have allowed the same to happen to her. She saw her mum's health deteriorate rapidly – and in particular, her memory worsened.

Looking back, there have been some extremely stressful times – like when Ruth's daughter gave birth to her first child while Edna was in hospital for 10 weeks in a diabetic coma. The effect of the accumulated strain, feels Ruth, was unfortunate. Despite enjoying a lifelong, close friendship with her mum, Ruth became less patient towards the end of the time spent caring for Edna at home. Exhausted, she frequently wished she could run away from the situation. This in turn made her feel guilty. Her emotions were in turmoil. Now she has to live with the disappointment of feeling she failed her mum, and the pain of watching her steady decline.

Making the necessary practical arrangements may help to keep your feelings at bay for a while, but you are likely eventually to confront a good deal of pain over the seeming finality of this process.

Try as you may, you cannot but feel you have somehow failed. You feel bitterly disappointed that, after perhaps years of struggling valiantly, you have not been able to avoid this undesirable outcome (as you see it). What began as an invigorating, rewarding challenge has gradually eroded your health. Instead of being able to congratulate yourself on a job well done, you feel you have given up. It may help to know that you are not alone in feeling guilt over moving your parent to a home. Perversely, it is probably those people who have tried the hardest to keep their parent at home, who then feel the most guilty about accepting what feels like defeat. And your parent may not soften the blow either. They may quite deliberately set out to make you feel bad about their plight. They may not accuse you in so many words; but a look in the eye of desolation or reluctant resignation may be enough to make you feel like the cruellest person on earth.

Try not to blame your parent for their feelings. It may help to remind yourself that moving to a home is a traumatic and stressful experience for them, however necessary. It may be something they have long dreaded and resisted. They may know in their heart of hearts that they will never be coming home again, and view the home as the last staging-post before death. They fear the experience of living in community, surrounded by people they do not know and may not like. They may worry about how easily they will be able to relate to other residents, especially those who are very ill.

Your parent may belong to a generation which associates old people's homes with the workhouse – a place of shame and stigma in which unfortunate older people with no alternative were forced to end their days during the nineteenth and early twentieth centuries. They may also have heard alarming reports of abuse and neglect in homes, and not realize that these cases represent only a minority of homes. Bad practice has often received undue attention in the media. While understanding your parent's sorrow and fear over moving to a home, you need to avoid being influenced by them. They will soon discover that their irrational fears are misplaced. It may take time, but eventually they will settle, and you can comfort yourself over the prospect of their receiving extensive medical help, and getting to know a wider circle of friends.

Inevitably you will feel a degree of anxiety over placing your parent in the care of an institution. Looking after them well has been a source of pride for you. Over the years, you have developed skills in nursing them. You know their needs intimately. You know how best to handle them without causing pain. You know which meals are most digestible and appetizing for them. You instinctively understand their preferred routine. You worry that staff in a home will not be able to offer the specialist support you can give, that they won't have the time to attend to the details which seem important to you.

It may be helpful, when choosing a home, to have an eye to the opinion held by staff over the role of relatives. A good home should see relatives as partners. Their first concern should be to discuss a resident's needs with the person who has been caring for them before admission. Staff should be anxious to make you feel involved, and to give you a special role within the home. They should be pleased to welcome you at any time you choose to visit. Check before selecting a home whether or not families are accommodated and made to feel important. That way you may save yourself some frustration and heartache later on.

On the other hand, however, you also need to exercise sensitivity. The staff who care for your parent don't want to feel that they are being told how to do their job. It may help to admit that there are several ways of caring, and that your way may not necessarily be better than another. Try to place your trust in your parent's carers. They will warm to your belief in them, and be more willing to take on board your suggestions. Part of you must accept that you are not the only person who can care well for your parent. This may be a painful discovery. Another part of you, however, needs to realize that staff in a nursing or residential home cannot offer the level and sensitivity of care given by a relative at home. Institutional living means that some aspects of individual care will be sacrificed. Staff ratios mean that care assistants cannot always be immediately available. Your parent may have to wait a few minutes until someone is free to help them go to the toilet, if the home is particularly busy.

If you are pained by what seem to be deficits in the care given to your parent by the home, try to remember that there are compensations. For one thing, your parent will be making new friends among staff and residents, whereas they may have been quite isolated while living at home. Your parent is now in a secure environment, with nursing support always on hand. They are well-fed and warm. Some homes have an extensive range of special activities, and arrange outings for residents. Your parent may have the opportunity to learn new skills. There may be concerts and parties for them to enjoy.

In reality, most people say that a care-home can never truly feel like 'home', and that they continue to miss their own home. But most are resigned to the fact that they need full-time care. They resolve to make the best of it, and can find many positives about their new environment. The misfortune for you is that any complaints they may have are saved for your visit. A stoical cheerfulness is probably presented the rest of the time – but you are treated to a litany of grievances. Very often, matrons and managers of homes understand this dynamic, and are keen to support families. It may be worth confiding in a member of staff, who can reassure you that your parent is actually reasonably contented after all.

Finding a new role

You can expect to feel at a loss following a parent's move to a care-home. The days may seem suddenly very long. Structure is lacking in your life. You no longer have intensive caring tasks as a focus. It is good to see this period as a type of bereavement. You may still have your parent, but you have lost a role towards them which has given your life meaning and motivation. Suddenly the future seems empty. You may not have expected to miss the caring so deeply.

Your first task is to negotiate a new role in supporting your parent. Their move to a home does not mark a complete break in your relations with them. The value of your contribution to their well-being is unchanged. You may no longer carry the full burden of physical care, but the underlying devotion and commitment remain. These were the aspects of your care for your parent that always mattered the most. In a sense, you can celebrate the fact that freedom from onerous nursing care allows you to concentrate on the emotional support and love you can uniquely give your parent.

Homes vary in the care they will allow you to continue to give. Some homes prefer relatives not to dress or feed their loved ones, but others don't mind. Some homes discourage relatives from visiting frequently early on, for fear of unsettling the new resident. Ultimately your wishes over visiting cannot be overruled. You know your parent best of all, and can judge how often it would be wise for you to visit. Frequent visiting can have its own impact, especially if it involves much travelling or distressing reminders of your grief and anxiety over your parent being in a home. Be careful not to over-tire yourself at this stage, when you are vulnerable and in need of time to recover from the rigours of caring. In many ways you need to see this time in your life as a period of recovery. Physically you may feel quite ill, as the accumulated strain catches up with you. You may feel the need to sleep all the time. Certainly you are likely to be emotionally fragile.

It may, then, be necessary to wait some considerable time before you resume activities which you shed upon becoming a carer. Perhaps you want to return to paid work, or there may be voluntary groups you would like to support. These activities will be helpful in filling the void left by caring, but ideally they should wait until you are fully fit.

Mike's parents married in 1939 but, because his father Tom served in the war, they were not able to start a family until 1946. Mike was their only child. Marjorie, Mike's mum, worked for the same firm as Tom. In fact, the company employed many local folk. By the time he retired, Tom had given 50 years' service.

Mike left home to study at university and then train as a teacher, but he sought a teaching post close to home and went back to live with Tom and Marjorie. He began his teaching career in a primary school in a neighbouring town, but was later to take up a job in the secondary school he had attended as a boy. Mike's relationship with both parents was warm and harmonious, but he was especially close to his mum.

For the first two years of retirement, Marjorie enjoyed a full and active life, taking part in afternoon classes and ladies' activities at her local church. Then, at the age of 62, she began to show signs of Alzheimer's disease. Between them, Mike and Tom managed to look after her, Mike giving his dad a break during school holidays by taking Marjorie for days out on the train. But in 1985, Tom died suddenly of a heart attack at the age of 71. Mike found him one morning in bed. Marjorie had been lying next to him, unaware that anything was wrong. Mike felt that the best way to help his mum understand that Tom had died was to take her with him each day to the funeral home, so that she could see he was no longer alive. She was able to express no grief and Mike still cannot know for sure whether she fully grasped the reality of her widowhood.

Life was then much harder for Mike. Continuing to teach full-time, he relied on social services' support. Marjorie attended two day-centres and, to guarantee her safety while alone in the house, Mike made sure there were no potential hazards. Fortunately, Marjorie did not wander too far from the house. The town in which they lived was a close-knit community, so a neighbour would tend to spot Marjorie and invite her in for a cup of tea while Mike was contacted. On occasions when she was not intercepted, Mike knew where to find her, because she would always head for the same place. Mike is grateful for the friends who took his mum with them to social events and meetings.

Working and caring were stressful, but Mike saw the teaching as a release. He also joined a carers group at the local psycho-geriatric hospital, and found the support of other carers invaluable. As they talked together about their experiences, they would learn from one another. Mike says he coped through hardening himself. Only through knuckling under and getting on with the task at hand was he able to live with the pressure he faced.

Nine years into Marjorie's illness, Mike's local social services department intervened, and suggested that it was perhaps time he considered finding a place for her in a home. After assessing Marjorie, they offered her a place and Mike accepted on her behalf. He was pleased with the quality of care she received, and the ease with which she settled into her new home. He was relieved to be able to pursue a new direction in his career, and began training as an Anglican priest.

After his mum had moved to the nursing home, Mike still needed help from the carers group to get in touch with his feelings, and enable him to deal with the pain of watching his mum deteriorate.

Marjorie and Mike's relationship was on a new footing. Mike

would visit as often as he could. They would walk together in the gardens of the home. Marjorie stayed physically fit until the last two years of her life. Then her health went downhill and she no longer recognized Mike as her son. Mike continued to visit faithfully, though, in the hope that there would be fleeting moments of awareness. Having been ordained by this stage, he would go in his dog collar and pray with Marjorie. Amazingly, she was still able to say the Lord's Prayer, having been a regular church-goer all her life. Sometimes the visits seemed pointless, but Mike could not stay away. Visiting gave him peace of mind.

Five years after moving to the nursing home, Marjorie died. For fourteen years of Mike's life, his time and energy were taken over by the illness which gradually took his dear mother from him. Still only 49, the illness cut across his young adult life. And yet, he has strangely never felt that life treated him unfairly. He feels that caring for his mum was something he did out of love and gratitude. It was the natural conclusion to a close and rewarding relationship.

Receiving support

You are not alone in having a relative in a home. Many people share the feelings you are experiencing. It may be helpful, then, to receive support from others in the same situation. The home in which your parent lives may have a relatives' group, which fulfils a role beyond merely raising funds for the home. There is also a new charity for people with elderly relatives in homes, called the Relatives Association. The Association has an information and advice service you can ring between 10 a.m. and 12.30 p.m., and 1.30 and 5 p.m., Monday to Thursday. The phone number is 0171 916 6055. The Relatives Association has a regular newsletter, and is also developing a network of local groups.

If you are worried in any way about the home where your parent lives, try not to ignore your fears. Sometimes relatives worry about complaining lest they invite the victimization of their parent. Homes have to establish a complaints procedure as part of the process of registering. The procedure should be advertised (often in the home's brochure or handbook). Usually your first course of action is to speak informally with a member of staff, perhaps your parent's key-worker if they have one, or the matron. They should investigate your concern and take any necessary action. If you are still unhappy, your next course of action is to contact the local inspection unit. Their address and phone number should be posted in a prominent place in the home. In all likelihood, these measures will not be necessary – but it is sensible to accept a role in monitoring your parent's care, and in making sure you approve of the treatment they receive. Older people in homes can be vulnerable to exploitation. You can have a valuable role in ensuring their safety and happiness.

Conclusion

It may be that you never thought to see a day when your parent moved to a care-home. Guilt and sorrow may fill your heart. Comfort yourself with the knowledge that you did all you could, and that your parent is now in the best possible place. Your love and commitment to them is as strong as ever, so you have no cause to condemn yourself. Nursing and residential homes are not places to be avoided. They can be places of great warmth and care, where older people flourish and find new quality of life in their closing days.

8

Recovery after caring

When a relative dies, a period of intense activity often follows. Arrangements must be made for the funeral. Relatives and friends must be contacted. Thought must be given to disposing of property. There is scarcely space to absorb the reality of your loss. Early on, support flows from many directions, with friends and relatives visiting to share your grief and offer condolences.

When the dust settles over your bereavement, and the visits become less frequent, however, it may dawn on you gradually that your parent's death represents a crisis which has left you reeling. Those around you may mistakenly consider the loss to be a welcome escape for you from the demands of caring. You may feel a pressure to move on, to put behind you the years of caring and find a new way of life. There is much for you to work through, however, before you can step out into the new world which awaits you. Now, perhaps more than ever, you need the support of good friends as you think back over the time spent caring, and come to terms with its ending. The stresses of caring may have long denied you the luxury of reflection, so now your mind is full of questions about what it has meant to commit yourself to your parent in their final years, and how the experience has altered your perspective.

Resolving how you feel about your caring may take many years. Recovering may be a surprisingly slow and painful ordeal. It may entail a confusing array of feelings. The following are pieces of advice which may help you come to terms with what has happened.

Recognize the extent of your loss

Loss becomes complicated in situations where the person who has died has needed care beforehand. Losing a parent can provoke tremendous feelings of fear and insecurity under any circumstances. Being 'orphaned', even as an adult, can leave us feeling alone and frightened, as we recognize that the steady, supportive parental influence is gone, and that there remain no generations now to separate us from the prospect of dying. We are next in line. We feel exposed and vulnerable.

Grief, however, has been a familiar companion for many carers for quite some time, as we saw in Chapter 5. With the finality of death, they have also to come to terms with the grief that has festered over their parent's steady decline and inexorable change. Many feel that they lost their parent long before their eventual death, because conditions like dementia had robbed them of all traces of their personality. In coming to terms with the loss through death of a parent, these carers must also work through the pain of having seen their parent's identity slowly eroded through the ravages of disease. Such long-standing anguish, now compounded by death, cannot easily be shaken off.

Loss is felt in another direction. As well as mourning the death of your parent, you may also miss the role you fulfilled towards them. Life can feel suddenly empty and meaningless without their needs to meet. Perhaps you have sacrificed many aspects of your former life through caring for your parent. You may have withdrawn from the labour market. Friendships may have lapsed. Your parent had become your entire life. Without them, you struggle to find vestiges of your own role in life. In an instant, you ceased to be a carer – or so it feels. You no longer have regular visits from the nurses, home-helps or care attendants who had become friends. You feel as though you have been dropped.

Others may consider your parent's death a merciful release for you – but you yourself feel you have been robbed of a cherished role, a way of life which, though difficult, had become second nature. Perhaps you recoil at the thought of once more having to earn a living. Having been based so exclusively at home, you may lack the confidence to venture into the public world of work, fearing that you no longer possess skills which will be of interest to employers.

No two carers respond alike to the death of their parent. Some cope better than others. It would not be unusual, however, for you to live with a profound sadness for several years afterwards. You may shed many tears, not only over the loss of your parent, but also over the memory of the pain and indignity they endured in their closing years. Elements of your grief may include a sense of anger over what has happened, or a measure of guilt over the care you gave. Initially, your response may be one of disbelief. All these are common reactions to bereavement, which can be heightened for carers.

It may seem irrational, but carers can feel angry that all their efforts have come to nothing, ending with the death of a person in whom they invested tremendous love and care. Some feel cross with their parent for abandoning them. Others feel bitter that they now have so little to show for their dedication, and are left with only the outcome of sacrifices it entailed. Guilt can be all too easily overwhelming, and is common to most bereavements. Carers overlook the kindness and concern which embodied the care they gave, and dwell instead on their failings. They cannot recall the provocation they received, only their anger and intemperate words. They feel distressed that there is now no opportunity to apologize for moments of weakness or intolerance, no chance to make amends.

Disbelief is also understandable. It can take a long time before a carer can accept that their parent has gone. They are instinctively programmed towards protecting and nurturing, and these drives are not quickly lost. Carers find themselves listening for their parent at night-time, rushing back home at the time their parent would have returned from day-centre, or storing up things to tell their parent. Many of these feelings cannot and should not be avoided. They are important dimensions of healthy grief, which you need to recognize as normal and natural. Time will heal the hurt eventually. It may be, however, that you need help in dealing with the complexities of your feelings. CRUSE offer skilled bereavement counselling, and can be contacted through your local Citizens' Advice Bureau or Council for Voluntary Service. Perhaps talking to a close friend or relative would be just as effective. Try not to suppress your feelings or bottle them up. It is far more therapeutic to let them out. A good friend will understand that you may need to go over the same feelings again and again. These feelings are unlikely to pass within weeks, or even months. Realistically you should expect that elements of your grief will remain raw for at least a year or two following your parent's death.

Christine cannot remember a time in her life when she knew true happiness. And neither does she expect that she will find it in the future. The first shattering blow came in 1971, when she was only 40, and her husband died suddenly of a heart attack, leaving her to provide and care for two daughters, aged 12 and 15 at the time. She had spent the first few years of her married life apart from him, as he worked in the Merchant Navy. Things had been tough then, as his wages had been very poor. It had been 12 years since Christine's parents moved from the countryside to live in the flat beneath their daughter's family home. Christine's dad was already ill at the time of her husband's death, and his health steadily deteriorated so that he died three years later, aged 87. Throughout his decline, Christine had helped her mum, Millie, nurse him. She shared her mum's stress and heartache over the effects of dementia and several strokes.

For a few years life was uneventful. In 1978, Christine decided to take a post as an auxiliary nurse in her local hospital, and found the work rewarding. But it was not long before her mum showed signs of developing Alzheimer's disease. How Christine wishes now that she had understood the effects of the illness. Perhaps she would not have taken to heart Millie's hurtful accusations. She could have been prepared to some extent for the transformation in personality she was to witness. Caring for her mum was painful and difficult for Christine. Although close to Millie, Christine had never received much warmth from her. Millie had been a harsh, domineering parent. Christine was thrown into bewildering turmoil when she found herself having to speak to her mum as though Millie were a young child. There was the occasion, for instance, when she discovered her mum at 3 a.m. frantically turning her bedroom upside-down in a futile search for something she had lost. Christine felt sickened at finding herself chiding her mum as though she were a naughty child, and telling her to go back to sleep.

In 1983, eight full years before retirement, Christine could cope no longer with the stress of working and caring for her mum. She felt she had no choice but to leave work and thrust herself into a position of financial insecurity in order to care adequately for her mum. But four years later, Christine's own health stopped her from being able to continue caring at home. After being in hospital with a hernia, she was forced to confront the awful truth that full-time caring was no longer possible for her. Being Millie's only child, she realized there was no alternative but to search for a suitable nursing home.

For Christine, the recognition that her mum needed nursing care was agonizing. It was not as if her mum had reached a stage in her illness where she had lost her awareness of what was happening around her. Christine knew that her mum had always sworn she would never go into a home, and would feel betrayed and abandoned by her own daughter. Visits to the home were devastating for Christine, as she witnessed the relentless decline in Millie's condition. After each visit she would leave in floods of tears. The guilt was unbearable, and compounded by the memory of occasions when, exhausted and under pressure, she had lost her patience and said things she now bitterly regretted. For four years she watched her mum slowly fade. For the final two, Millie did not recognize her, though she seemed to sense that she was someone special.

Millie died in 1991 at the age of 93. Christine has needed several years of rest and regular counselling before feeling able even to consider embarking on anything new. Until quite recently, she was unable to talk about her mum's illness without crying, such was the pain she felt over the effects of the Alzheimer's on Millie's final years. Writing down her feelings, both while her mum was living and since her death, has been a great solace. She has recently had poems included in anthologies. There have been plenty of days when, weighed down with sadness and guilt, she has considered suicide. But she jokes that, instead of reaching for the bottle, she reaches for her pen and finds relief in noting down how she feels.

Never having been a strong person, Christine (now 64) was recently diagnosed as having osteoporosis. She has had several falls recently. And the demands on her emotional energies continue. Both of her daughters are in difficult relationships, with one in particular leaning heavily on Christine for support. She feels her life is little more than existence, but caring for her family gives her the will to carry on. She hopes that she may one day have the strength to offer counselling to other people with emotional problems.

Expect exhaustion

Not everyone has the luxury of time to recover and renew their strength following the death of a parent for whom they have cared. Some find that the loss of social security benefits leaves them perilously close to financial ruin, so that a return to paid work is a priority. If you are in a position which allows you to delay or avoid returning to work, you are fortunate, because many former carers find their strength and health at a low ebb. It takes a while for them to recharge their batteries and feel able to engage in new activities.

You perhaps were unable or unwilling to grasp how tired you were becoming as you nursed your parent. The years of broken nights, the stress of practical demands, the intensity of emotional issues, may have contributed to a drain on your resources. While your parent was alive, you had reason to dig very deeply into those reserves of energy. Now they no longer need your support, however, you are paying the price. Sheer exhaustion overwhelms and envelops you. Years of pushing yourself mercilessly have finally caught up on you. Your may feel you want to do nothing but sleep. Or perhaps you find it impossible to summon the motivation needed even for simple tasks.

The unfortunate few succumb to complete collapse after their parent dies. For some this has mainly physical manifestations, involving a catalogue of illness. For others, there is nervous collapse – a sinking into severe depression, perhaps. What kind of a reward is this, many cry, for years of unstinting devotion? Strange though it may seem, it helps to regard bereavement after caring as a period of convalescence. Like someone recovering from illness or surgery, you need to allow yourself plenty of rest and sleep, fresh air, or perhaps a holiday. You are not weak and ineffectual in needing this space to heal and prepare for the future. You are merely human. Your body needs conditions which will help restore it after years of superhuman effort. It probably feels strange to be idle. You are accustomed through caring to a regime of hard work and constant activity. It may take time for you to adjust to the new, slower pace of life. You may be tempted to throw yourself into new roles, in order perhaps to avoid some of the painful feelings which threaten to engulf you. Time spent resting, and confronting how you feel, will be time well spent. It will equip you with new strength, enabling you to face the future and make far better decisions than if you were to rush headlong into what lies ahead.

Give it time

Losing your parent is known as a 'major life event', something which involves a high degree of stress and requires major adjustment. Dealing with your grief at the same time as recovering from a potential wave of exhaustion cannot be accomplished quickly. Time is of the essence. To expect to be able to bounce back is unrealistic. Besides, you need time to establish how your life has changed as a result of caring for your parent.

Caring tends not to be an experience which touches people lightly. It can produce great changes in an individual. It can alter personality, and it can shape a person's world-view. Caring builds character – of that there can be little doubt. It can produce incredible stamina, and can cultivate qualities which previously lay dormant – such as patience, tolerance and kindness. In addition, caring can alter radically the way in which a person looks at life. Things which had seemed of ultimate importance lose some of their meaning. New priorities emerge. New gifts are born. These changes are hearteningly positive, and can amount to a force for love and compassion in society.

Because caring turns lives upside-down in this way, carers can feel indecisive over choices they must make following bereavement. The idea of returning to their former area of work may seem strange. Besides the fear that skills have been lost, there can also be the sense that a previous role no longer fits with aspirations born out of caring. You may feel that you have moved on, that your former career is part of your past now, not something to which you wish to return. You may hope for a new direction, which can encompass and incorporate the skills learned while caring for your parent. Many carers choose to retrain and gain skills for a new job. Others decide to invest their time and commitment in voluntary work.

The process of discovering a new way of life, post-caring, is likely to require not only intense thought but also detailed discussion with the people close to you. Spending time talking with friends and relatives can help you to work out the ways in which caring has altered your perspective, and to decide upon a future role. It may be that you prefer to talk with a counsellor about how you feel. Counsellors are available through the NHS via your GP or through charitable groups (contact your Citizens' Advice Bureau for information).

The key is to avoid rushing into a new role, if at all possible. Try not to feel guilty about giving yourself time to reflect. Don't allow yourself to be pressurized by others into hasty decisions. People around you may be well-meaning in their advice. They may have genuinely good motives in pressing you into new activities. At the end of the day, though, the choices must be yours – however long it takes to reach them.

Anne married into a large family. Her husband, Keith, was one of seven boys and a girl, and Anne established her home with him a couple of doors from where her mother-in-law lived, in a small, close-knit village. Even before her two sons were born, Anne offered a little help to Keith's mum, Jessie, popping round each Monday morning to peg out her washing.

Anne's involvement grew gradually and steadily over the years. She and her sisters-in-law took it in turns to cook Jessie's meals. A deterioration in Jessie's mental health coincided with the death in quick succession of three of her sons. Signs of dementia began to appear. Anne says she became 'stroppy'. A bed was moved downstairs into her front room, and an alarm bell fitted which rang in Anne and Keith's house. Several incidents heightened anxiety over the old lady's safety. Because Anne and Keith's house had the same lay-out as Jessie's, it was decided that she would move in with them. Their front room became 'Nan's room'. Anne and Keith took it in turns to look after her, with Keith taking over for the 'evening shift' on his return from work, handing over again to Anne at 1 a.m..

Anne feels that carers in small villages have special problems. Older village folk tend to be proud and self-reliant, unwilling to receive help for fear of what neighbours might think. Services often fail to reach outlying areas. Anne herself received help only once a week (reduced to once a fortnight when resources dwindled) from an auxiliary nurse who would wash her mum. Bus services to remote villages are infrequent, so fetching medication is difficult. And there is little a carer can do to take their mind off their troubles when caring becomes too much – no shops to browse through, few parks to walk in . . .

Although it was hard work caring for her mother-in-law while raising her own children, Anne genuinely appreciated Jessie. She found the old lady's advice invaluable and was pleased that her sons were so close to their grandmother. She describes Jessie as a strong, dominant character, who commanded respect and esteem, and kept her family together. During the four years Jessie lived with her, there were many moments when Anne would gladly have given in to the older lady's pleas to be allowed to die. Anne understood Jessie's desperate desire to be spared the humiliation and indignity she increasingly experienced. Anne found Jessie's final eight weeks in hospital particularly painful. To see the parent she loved fading gradually at the age of 88, refusing to eat and sinking into a coma, was almost more than she could bear.

Even four years after Jessie's death, Anne still finds herself unable to shake off the feelings of responsibility she carried for 15 years. She still wakes in the early hours, ready for her night-time vigil, and catches herself preparing to share news with Jessie. She is saddened to find that the wider family are now less close, having lost a focal point. Her front room is still 'Nan's room' and she cannot bring herself to throw away Jessie's possessions.

Anne is still a carer. Her youngest son has severe seizures which have left him with brain damage. He attended a special school, but now he is 21 there is no support available for him near to home, and little prospect of him finding work. Anne sees her role as helping other carers. She runs a support group for carers from the local villages. She acknowledges that theirs was never a normal family life, but asks herself 'What is normal anyway?'

Look for continuity

Carers vary in the extent to which they crave a continuation of their caring role. Some are happy that a chapter in their lives has closed. They long for the tonic of something fresh and new, a contrast with the role they fulfilled in nursing a parent. Others feel insecure, and look fretfully for ways in which they can continue with the only role they now know, that of caring for elderly relatives; they become 'career carers', moving from one relative, friend or neighbour to the next, and depending unhealthily on this role. For others, however, there is a middle road to be found. While not wishing to perpetuate their direct caring role, they nevertheless desire a new way of life which allows them to exercise the many skills they have developed through caring.

You may have discovered you have a talent for looking after people with disabilities. Caring for them may bring you a fulfilment you never imagined possible. You may have learned a depth of empathy and compassion which you wish to put to good use. Finding an element of continuity with the past in this way can be most helpful. It may involve acquiring new qualifications, or entering an unfamiliar area of work. Have the courage of your convictions. Caring has equipped you with a special expertise which will enable you to perform your new role with commitment and success.

One response to the experience of caring can be a desire for some sort of role which enables a former carer to help other carers. This may amount to no more than befriending carers with whom they come into contact. It may entail volunteering for a charitable project which aims to support carers. For many, though, it has led to applying for a paid post as a carers' support worker. Former carers have a unique insight which equips them marvellously for this role. Caring can only be fully understood by those who have been through it. It can, therefore, be a great relief to be able to confide in someone who has encountered similar stresses and difficulties.

You should not feel pressurized into a supportive role, and certainly not before you are ready to cope with the demands involved. You may, however, find it therapeutic to make life easier for other carers, and offer them the support that perhaps you lacked.

Conclusion

With the death of your parent, it may feel that the bottom has fallen out of your world. The pain of missing them may be hard to bear. You have the comfort, though, of knowing that you gave yourself to their care. Your love and commitment helped to ease the distress and difficulties of their final years. Life will never be the same again. The world is shaded in different colours. Eventually the intensity of grief will pass. Your new skills, however, will remain and will continue to be a resource within your family and community. Perhaps you wonder if it was all worth the cost in the end. You may never know. You will not receive any medals. Public recognition is unlikely to be forthcoming. You may well have bid farewell to dreams, and missed out on opportunities.

Though thanks may not be yours for now, a reward may await you once the gloom of death has lifted, your prize the discovery of a new self, with firm convictions and compelling motivations. The benefit you have gained could well be the discovery that you are someone with the capacity to care in the face of overwhelming odds. You may eventually be able to thank your parent for helping you to see what really matters in life, and to learn a new and enduring depth of warmth and compassion. No experience is wasted, and in time – if not at present – you will see what caring has taught you. My hope is that the bequest your parent has left you will be one that you can treasure.

Useful organizations

Age Concern
Astral House
1268 London Road
London SW16 4ER
0181 679 8000

Age Concern Cymru
4th Floor, 1 Cathedral Road
Cardiff CF1 9SD
01222 371566

Age Concern Scotland
113 Rose Street
Edinburgh EH2 3DT
0131 220 3345

Alzheimer's Disease Society
Gordon House
10 Greencoat Place
London SW1 1PH
0171 306 0606

**Alzheimer's Disease Society
Scotland**
8 Hill Street
Edinburgh EH2 3JZ
Helpline: 0131 220 6155

Arthritis Care
18 Stephenson Way
London NW1 2HD
0171 916 1500
Helpline: 0800 289170

**Association of Crossroads Care
Attendant Schemes**
10 Regent Place
Rugby
Warwickshire CV21 2PN
01788 573 653

**Association of Crossroads Care
Attendant Schemes, Wales**
Unit 5, Coopers Yard
Curran Road
Cardiff CF1 5DF
01222 222282

**BACUP (British Association of
Cancer United Patients)**
3 Bath Place
Rivington Street
London EC2A 3JR
0171 613 2121
*Helpline: 0800 181 199 (callers
from outside London)*

**Benefit Enquiry Line: 0800
882200**

British Heart Foundation
14 Fitzhardinge Street
London W1H 4DH
0171 935 0185

British Lung Foundation
New Garden House
78 Hatton Gardens
London EC1N 8JR
0171 831 5831

Cancer Relief Macmillan Fund
Anchor House
15–19 Britten Street
London SW3 3TZ
0171 351 7811

CancerLink
17 Britannia Street
London WC1X 9JN
0171 833 2451
MAC Helpline for Adolescents:
0800 591028
AsianLine: 0171 713 7867

Cancerlink Scotland
9 Castle Terrace
Edinburgh EH1 2DP
0131 228 5557

Carers Christian Fellowship
Mrs Brenda Baalham
14 Yealand Drive
Ulverston
Cumbria LA12 9JB
01229 585974

Carers National Association
20–25 Glasshouse Yard
London EC1A 4JS
0171 490 8818
CarersLine: 0171 490 8898

Carers National Association, Scotland
11 Queen's Crescent
Glasgow G4 9AS
0141 333 9495

Carers National Association, Wales
Pantglas Industrial Estate
Bedwas
Newport
Gwent NP1 8DR
01222 880176

Counsel and Care for the Elderly
Twyman House
16 Bonny Street
London NW1 9PG
0171 458 1566

Crossroads (England & Wales)
see under Association of
Crossroads Care Attendant
Schemes

Crossroads (Scotland) Care Attendant Schemes
24 George Street
Glasgow G2 1EG
0141 226 3793

CRUSE (Bereavement Care)
126 Sheen Road
Richmond
Surrey TW9 1UR
0181 940 4818

CRUSE, Scotland
18 South Trinity Road
Edinburgh EH5 3PN
0131 551 1511

CRUSE, Wales
Mrs Joan Morgan
Old Bedw Farmhouse
Near Erwood
Builth Wells
Powys LD2 3LQ
01982 560468

Dial UK (Disablement Information and Advice Line)
Park Lodge
St Catherine's Hospital
Tickhill Road
Balby
Doncaster DN4 8QN
01302 310123

Disability Scotland
Princes House
5 Shandwick Place
Edinburgh EH2 4RG
0131 229 8632

Elderly Accommodation Counsel
(Helping older people find accommodation)
46A Chiswick High Road
London W4 1SZ
0181 742 1182 or 0181 995 8320

Help the Aged
St James's Walk
London EC1R 0BE
0171 253 0253
SeniorLine: 0800 650065

Help the Aged, Scotland
Herriot House
Herriot Hill Terrace
Edinburgh EH7 4DY
0131 556 4666

Holiday Care Service
2nd Floor, Imperial Buildings
Victoria Road
Horley
Surrey RH6 7PZ
01293 774535

Hospice Information Service
St Christopher's Hospice
51–59 Lawrie Park Road
Sydenham
London SE26 6DZ
0181 778 9252

MIND (National Association for Mental Health)
Granta House
15–17 Broadway
Stratford
London E15 4BQ
0181 519 2122

MIND, Wales
23 St Mary Street
Cardiff
South Glamorgan CF1 2AA
01222 395123

Marie Curie Cancer Care
28 Belgrave Square
London SW1X 8QG
0171 235 3325

Marie Curie Scotland
21 Rutland Street
Edinburgh EH1 2AE
0131 229 8332

Parkinson's Disease Society
22 Upper Woburn Place
London WC1H 0RA
0171 383 3513

Partially Sighted Society
Queen's Road
Doncaster
South Yorkshire DN1 2NX
01302 323132

Princess Royal Trust for Carers
16 Byward Street
Tower Hill
London EC3R 5BA
0171 480 7788

RADAR (Royal Association for Disability and Rehabilitation)
Unit 12
City Forum
250 City Road
London EC1V 8AF
0171 250 3222

The Relatives Association
(For relatives and friends of older people in homes)
5 Tavistock Place
London WC1H 9SN
0171 916 6055

Royal National Institute for the Deaf
105 Gower Street
London WC1E 6AH

Royal National Institute for the Deaf, Scotland
9 Clairmont Gardens
Glasgow G3 7LW
0141 332 0343

Royal National Institute for the Blind (RNIB)
224 Great Portland Street
London W1N 6AA
0171 388 1266

RNIB, Scotland (Resource Centre)
9 Viewfield Place
Stirling FK8 1NL
01786 451752

RNIB, Wales
4th Floor, 33–35 Cathedral Road
Cardiff
South Glamorgan CF1 2HB
01222 668606

Stroke Association
CHSA House
123–127 Whitecross Street
London EC1Y 8JJ
0171 490 7999

Wales Council for the Deaf
Maritime Offices
Woodland Terrace
Maesycoed
Pontypridd
Mid Glamorgan CF37 1DZ
01443 485687

Further reading

Brown, Paul, *Pensioners and Carers*. Directory of Social Change, 1995.

Horwood, Janet, *Caring: How to Cope*. Health Education Authority, 1994.

Kohner, Nancy, *Caring at Home: A Handbook for People Looking After Someone at Home*. Kings Fund Informal Caring Programme/NEC, 1988 (available by contacting NEC directly on 01223 450283).

Lewis, Jane and Meredith, Barbara, *Daughters Who Care*. Routledge, 1988.

Orton, Christine, *Care for the Carer: Make Life Easier, Happier and More Fulfilling – For You and the Elderly Person You Look After*. Thorsons, 1989.

Pitkeathley, Jill, *It's My Duty, Isn't It? The Plight of Carers in Our Society*. Souvenir Press, 1989.

Qureshi, Hazel and Walker, Alan, *The Caring Relationship: Elderly People and Their Families*. Macmillan, 1989.

Streater, Osman, *Loving Care: Essential Guidance for Those With Elderly Parents*. N & P Publishing, 1993.

Thompson, Dr Keith, *Caring for an Elderly Relative*. Optima Positive Health Guides, 1986.